STO ✓

The World of the Opossum

A LIVING WORLD BOOK

John K. Terres, Editor

The World of the Beaver by Leonard Lee Rue III

The World of the Black Bear by Joe Van Wormer

The World of the Bobcat by Joe Van Wormer

The World of the Coyote by Joe Van Wormer

The World of the Great Horned Owl
    by G. Ronald Austing and John B. Holt, Jr.

The World of the Opossum by James F. Keefe
    with photographs by Don Wooldridge

The World of the Porcupine by David F. Costello

The World of the Raccoon by Leonard Lee Rue III

The World of the Red-tailed Hawk by G. Ronald Austing

The World of the White-tailed Deer
    by Leonard Lee Rue III

The World of the Woodchuck by W. J. Schoonmaker

THE WORLD OF THE OPOSSUM

By James F. Keefe

with photographs by Don Wooldridge

J. B. LIPPINCOTT COMPANY
PHILADELPHIA AND NEW YORK

G 1575344

To my wife, for patience above and beyond . . .

Contents

Meet the Opossum   13

Spring   32

Summer   51

Autumn   72

Winter   93

The Opossum and Man   108

Opossum Subspecies   133

Bibliography   135

Index   141

THE WORLD OF THE OPOSSUM

Meet the Opossum

OVER THE YEARS the opossum and I have met many times and in many situations. I've seen him by flashlight as the dogs clamored around the sapling persimmon tree, I've seen him scuttle across highways in the headlights of my car, and often I've seen his battered carcass along the roadside. Almost anyone in the United States, except in the most arid parts of the West, has the opportunity to meet the opossum.

Those who may never have seen the animal face to face know him from stories and folk tales, for the opossum has enriched our history in many ways. A great deal that we read and hear is false, for scarcely any other of our common animals is as misunderstood. But no matter how unusual the tales told of the opossum, the truth is stranger yet; no other animal of our American fauna is as odd in so many ways.

Columbus discovered this hemisphere in 1492, and Vincente Yáñez Pinzón, who was a brother to one of Columbus's navigators, brought the first opossum to Spain in 1500, according to Peter Martyr, the Italian courtier and historian. He described it but did not use any name. The German, Konrad Gessner, gave the opossum its first European name in his book, *Historiae Animalium,* of 1558. He called it *simia vulpina,* or "monkey fox."

We have to thank Captain John Smith, whose head was saved by the Indian princess Pocahontas, for giving us our word "opossum." Smith probably asked an Algonquian-speaking Indian the name of the animal and the Indian answered "pasum" or "possum," but it was preceded by a grunt, so we've been plagued with the Irish-sounding appellation opossum ever since.

The Spanish, who were here long before Captain John Smith, had

13

Opossum in persimmon tree.

been collecting a long list of names for the opossum from various Indian tribes in Central and South America, for the animal is found on all the western continents. To the Aztec it was *tlaquatzin,* and the modern Mexican name still rings familiar as *tlacuache.* The Mayans called the opossum *och,* while in Brazil it was called *serwoy.* Carl G. Hartman lists a host of other names, from both North and South America, and even from Europe: *carigua, sarigoi, cerigoni, sarique, tai-ibi, churcha, zurcan, chincha, boschrot* or *boschratze* ("bush rat" in Dutch New Guinea), *rat de bois* (Louisiana), *rat de fôret* (French Guiana), *pia* or *puant, comedreya, micure* ("stinker" in Argentina), *gamba, sariqueya, faras, revales, zorro* or *zorro pelon, raposa, guica, quica, juron, shukata* or *shookhuta* (Choctaw), *cheera* (Tuscarora), *seequa* (Cherokee), *woa-pink* ("white face" in Lenape), and even *simivulpa* or Gessner's *simia vulpina.*

With so many common, or local, names, the opossum illustrates vividly why we have scientific names in Latin or Greek for all of this world's creatures. Once an animal or plant has a published scientific name, that becomes the name whereby it is known to other scientists all over the world.

A Swede named Carl von Linné founded the present-day system of

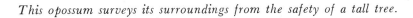

This opossum surveys its surroundings from the safety of a tall tree.

scientific names, bringing order out of chaos. We laymen will continue to say raccoon instead of *Procyon lotor,* bear instead of *Ursus americanus,* and dog for *Canis familiaris.* That's all right as long as we are conversing in our own language with our own countrymen. But should we need to talk about raccoons, bears, and dogs to those of other lands, we need a name understood by all, and here is where the generally accepted Latin name comes into use.

The opossum's scientific name, *Didelphis marsupialis,* is part Greek and part Latin. *Didelphis* means "double womb" in Greek and refers to either the opossum's paired uteri or possibly to the pouch serving as

The opossum's front foot. *The hind foot. Note opposable nailless "thumb," a great aid in climbing.*

The front feet leave tracks in snow like little stars.

an accessory "womb." *Marsupialis* is of Latin origin and means "pertaining to the pouch." Thus a literal translation of the opossum's scientific name would be "double womb of the pouch," which is almost as meaningless as some of the names we've misgathered from the Indians. It does point out one thing about opossums that has been of considerable interest to us: the pouch for carrying young.

There are a number of animals called opossums or possums, but we're considering here our North American opossum, or Virginia opossum, as it is sometimes called. It isn't an especially handsome animal (unless you happen to be another opossum), being about the size of a medium house cat, with long, coarse fur. Many consider it rather ratlike, with its long, slender, pointed muzzle, black eyes, prominent, thin, naked ears, and naked, scaly tail. Ernest Thompson Seton, a famed American naturalist, tells us that the Santee Sioux name for the opossum meant "big rat." It has five clawed toes on its front feet; each hind foot has

17

four toes with claws and a large, thumblike, clawless toe that opposes the other four. Its feet make characteristic tracks in soft mud, the prints of the front feet looking rather starlike and the tracks of the back feet like a monkey's footprints.

There is a prominent fur-lined pouch on the belly of the mature female. Both males and females are colored alike, being mostly grayish-white with the front and hind quarters darker and the belly lighter. As with most fur-bearing animals, the opossum's fur is of two types, coarse guard hairs and underfur. Most other Didelphid relatives of the opossum have no guard hairs. The guard hairs of the opossum are white, while the underfur is pure white and white tipped with black. The head is mostly white, though at times it may be yellowish. Also, at times the fur around the eyes may appear dusky. The nose is pink, the naked ears mostly black. The tail may be black from the base to almost half its length, then yellowish-white to pink the rest of its length. Feet and toes are pink to white.

The sparsely haired tail is rather ratlike and colored almost half of the way.

Meet the Opossum

Opossums are from 24 to 34 inches in length, with males usually larger than females. The tail makes up from 10 to 13 inches of the total length. Weight varies from four to fifteen pounds.

The opossum's tail has been the object of a good deal of misunderstanding. The ratlike appendage is described as prehensile, which means "grasping." In a sense this is true, but earlier writers tended to let their imaginations run away with them or to accept native reports too uncritically. The opossum can grasp objects with its tail, but it is a long way from being an extra hand.

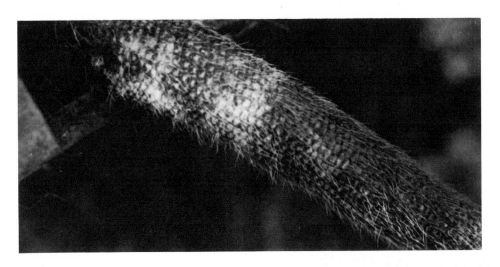

Close-up of opossum tail.

The typical opossum tail is carried with a downward curl near the blunt end. Carl G. Hartman says an upturning tail means the opossum is near death, and that the healthy opossum never carries its tail other than with a downward curl. The tip touches the ground as the opossum moves about, possibly serving as some sort of tactile organ. It really most comes into play when the opossum climbs, which it does very well. An opossum feeding on persimmons on a bright moonlit night wraps its tail lightly around limbs as it forages. It rarely, if ever, hangs by its

19

Fearful and at bay after being overtaken in snow. Note characteristic way of carrying tail, tip down.

tail; opossums seem to lose their hanging ability as they grow. Just as tiny human babies are able to support themselves hanging by their hands, so young opossums can wrap their tails around a right-sized limb and hang, though they must be made to do so. As they get older and larger, the ratio of tail strength to total body weight must become too great, and the ability to hang by the tail becomes less and less. Adults can support their weight by their tails only for a short time.

The opossum tail has been observed in use in an interesting nest-building activity, however. Back in 1872 G. Lincecum wrote of having seen opossums carrying leaves in their tails which they used to line their nests. In 1941, Luther Smith reported how opossums loaded this "fifth

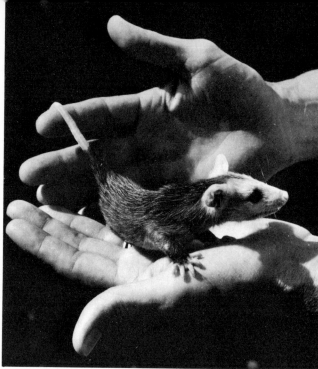

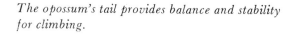

The opossum's tail provides balance and stability for climbing.

Note how this baby uses its tail as a grip.

hand" when he described an opossum that he saw in the Missouri woods.

About six or eight mouthfuls were handled in this way. The action was rapid, and the leaves were in almost continuous motion from the time they were picked up from the ground until they came to rest in the coil of the tail. After the loop was filled, the opossum chose a last mouthful, and, with its tail extended almost horizontally except for the loop which held the bundle of leaves, proceeded into the hole in the ground.

The animal came out of a hole in the ground about eight feet from where I stood, and proceeded to select small mouthfuls of two or three leaves each. The leaves were taken out of the mouth by the forepaws and passed back along the abdomen to a position in front of the thighs. There they remained momentarily while the front feet were placed on the ground and the hind feet were brought up to take them and slide them along the tail into a loop in that member, which is ordinarily thought of as a means of support by suspension but which in this case was sustaining the hind quarters above the ground while the hind feet were being used to place the leaves in the loop.

Soon the animal returned, and when it first came up the tail was

21

The opossum had to be posed for this picture, as it rarely hangs by the tail voluntarily.

nearly straight with the end dragging on the ground. When first leaves were picked up, the loop was formed in the tail, and the process of gathering a bundle of leaves was repeated. The opossum made four trips in about ten minutes.

This use of the tail to carry nest material has been observed by others. Marsupials other than the opossum have been reported to do this, too. Photographer Don Wooldridge had a young male opossum raised by his

22

The back feet are used to feed leaves back to the curled tail, where they are held and carried to the den.

daughters, which he used for a model. This particular animal was called Philbert, and he was one of nine rescued by youngsters when his mother was accidentally killed. The nine orphans were quickly scattered among a lot of foster homes, Philbert ending up at the Wooldridges'. Poor Philbert not only had to survive orphaning but also the almost too solicitous care of his foster parents. Somehow he did survive and actually flourished on the Wooldridges' side porch, growing into a husky, glossy-furred adolescent all one summer and fall. He had a fine nest box on the porch, lined with comfortable rags, and could roam the entire length of the porch. The girls had thoughtfully covered the porch floor with newspapers, which Philbert put to use one chilly autumn afternoon.

Don came home to be greeted by the girls and urged to come see what Philbert was up to. There on the porch Philbert was responding to some ancient urge. Though he had a comfortable nest already, the first cold day of autumn seemed to have triggered something inside him. In his odd way, he had torn up shreds of newspaper and put them into

23

Opossum carrying dry leaves for nesting material in its tail.

a loop of his tail. He didn't know what to do next, however, and kept wandering aimlessly around the porch, carrying his bundle of newspaper clippings.

Poor Philbert's tail was his undoing; later that winter it was frozen and developed gangrene. Despite the ministrations of a veterinarian, Philbert died, as must countless thousands of his brothers and sisters, for frozen ears and tails are commonplace in the opossum world.

Philbert isn't the first of his tribe to filch paper for a nest, however. There is a New Zealand story of a purloined five-pound note, missing from a lumber camp, that was eventually found in the nest of a brush-tailed marsupial "rat," and pieces of paper and rag seemed to have often been taken by these creatures for nesting material.

24

Meet the Opossum

Of all the various higher animals that roam our woods, the opossum is one the most silent. Although it has the usual voice apparatus, it seldom makes any sounds other than a faint hissing and, on rare occasions, a low growl. A young female opossum with nine young that I once kept used to growl occasionally when I would chase her into the nest

An angry opossum can be a fearful sight to the uninitiated.

The questing pink nose and beady black eyes are used to best advantage at night.

box inside her cage. I'd push her with a stick to get her into the den, so that I could clean the cage. She would merely open her mouth and drool at first, but when I'd finally urge her into the box she would growl at me from safely inside. If I didn't know opossums better I'd have been intimidated by that growl, but opossums aren't really aggressive enough to frighten anyone who knows them.

Her tiny young made a peculiar hiss, when separated from the mother, that sounded rather like air escaping in jets from an air hose. At mating time opossums commonly make a clicking sound with teeth or tongue; otherwise the opossum is, as Ernest Thompson Seton described it, an animal that "lays low and says nuffin'."

An opossum's sense of smell is very keen, as is his eyesight at night. The black, beady eyes seem to be all pupil, for the iris does not show at all, except in the brightest light, which the opossum avoids. The wide-open pupil, of course, speaks for the opossum's habits, which are almost entirely nocturnal. In daylight the opossum's vision does not appear especially sharp. We must assume that its sense of hearing is keen, based on observations of its behavior when it hears someone approach. The opossum is so lethargic, though, that it is sometimes hard to judge its reactions.

Slow-wittedness, or a lower "I.Q.," runs in the marsupial family, for almost all the tribe have small brains and exhibit very few of the traits we associate with intelligence in the higher animals.

Many years ago Vernon Bailey, Chief Field Naturalist of the U. S. Biological Survey, did an experiment to compare the brain size of the opossum with that of a raccoon. He filled the brain case of an opossum skull with beans and did the same with that of a raccoon. The opossum's brain case held only 21 beans, while the raccoon's held 150. The relatively small brain size is characteristic of the marsupials as a group. The genial and lovable raccoon's skull is about the same size as the opossum's, and there can be no doubt that the impish curiosity and intelligence of the raccoon is related to the much greater brain capacity of its skull.

Scientists have theorized about intelligence in animals, and crude attempts to measure it have been made. Most such studies merely confirm what general observations have led us to believe: some animals appear to be much smarter than others. If we agree that intelligence in wild animals is the ability to avoid danger, find food, and solve the immediate problems of living, we would think that the animal with the superior brain would have the greatest chance of survival. But nothing in nature is that simple. Both the raccoon, which we generally agree is

27

a very intelligent animal, and the opossum, which we generally agree is duller of wit, have not only survived from pre-Ice Age times but in the recent past have multiplied their numbers rapidly and spread their range north and westward. This indicates success in meeting life's problems. With the opossum, at least, its success in reproducing itself would appear to be more a factor than its intelligence. Its frontal lobes, with which intelligence is linked, are woefully deficient.

The opossum's pouch for carrying young is common to a group of animals we call "marsupials," meaning "animals with pouches." They are mammals, which means they are animals that possess hair at some time in their lives, have milk or mammary glands, and nurse their young. The word "mammals" is derived from the word "mammae," or "breasts."

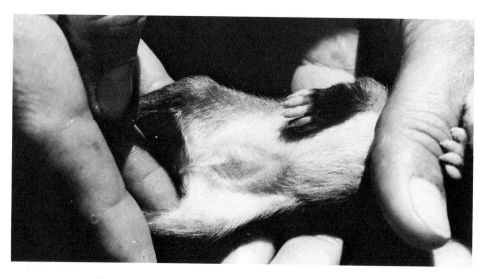

The tiny pouch shows that this baby is a female.

Hair covering is not dense in all mammals—for example, it is exceedingly scanty in many marine mammals—but traces of hair are present in all at some time in their lives. This is true even of whales, which, like other mammals, possess mammary glands that secrete milk for their

28

young. The female opossum usually has 13 mammae or teats located on her belly inside the pouch.

Actually the opossum is a rather primitive form of mammal, there being only one other group of mammals more so—the group containing the Australian duckbill, or platypus, and the spiny anteater. These creatures, although possessing hair and mammary glands, lay eggs, which they incubate in pouches. The opossum, as we shall see later, bears its young alive, though in embryonic form, which is typical of the marsupials as a group; the young mature in the pouch.

Besides the presence of a pouch in the female marsupials, two other oddities occur in their make-up that set them apart from other mammals. These are the presence of two bones attached to the pelvic bones, which help hold up the pouch, and a peculiar in-turning of the back part of the lower jaw. These the opossum has in common with other marsupials, but they are absent in higher mammals.

Most of the world's marsupials live in the Australian region west to the Celebes and Moluccas and in North and South America. They have been introduced into New Zealand. None occur naturally on the Eurasian land mass.

Aside from the aborigines and their dingo dogs—and some bats and rodents—marsupials were the highest form of animal life in Australia before the white man arrived. In that country, where placental mammals did not evolve, the marsupials branched into many forms, tending to fill almost every available life niche. Some were arboreal, spending most or all their lives in trees, like the tree kangaroos, koalas, and the gliding possums, which, except for size, are very similar to our flying squirrels. Some lived on the great plains, like the great gray kangaroo, and other species lived in rain forests and in deserts and along sea coasts. There were marsupials that acted like rabbits, and some that occupied ecological niches of woodchucks; some were marsupial wolves, and others, like the great kangaroos, took the place of grazing animals such as our bison. Some marsupials were burrowing animals, too. Their diets showed as much variety as those of the placental mammals, with some eating vegetable food, some eating only meat, and some being insect eaters.

It was once argued that Australia and South America must have formerly had some land connection because of their marsupial populations. Nowadays scientists generally believe the marsupials of both continents merely evolved from more widespread primitive forms common to both continents.

Our American opossum, of which a subspecies was first described from Virginia in 1792, has a counterpart in the scaly-tailed possum of western Australia. Captain Cook gave the name "opossums" to the ring-tailed opossums at Cooktown in 1770 because of their superficial resemblance to the Virginia opossum. Today the name "possum" in that country down under is applied indifferently to about seventeen genera and forty-two species of phalangers, cuscuses, and possums. Scientists generally use the term "possum" for the Australian forms and "opossum" for those of the Americas.

Almost all the Australian possums are arboreal, living most of their lives in trees. Many are more like squirrels than our shuffling opossum. One or two forms live in treeless areas, using other animals' burrows or caves or crevices, but most seldom descend from trees. Some are valuable fur bearers. All the females have well-defined pouches, with mammae. None of the Australian possums are at all closely related to our Virginia opossum, sharing only the name and the fact that they belong to the same great order of mammals.

The Virginia opossum belongs to a family of marsupials called the Didelphidae, which is composed of twelve genera and about sixty-five species. All live in North, Central, and South America only. Didelphids are known from southeastern Canada southward through the eastern United States and Mexico and into South America to about 47 degrees south latitude in Argentina. Other forms of the so-called Virginia opossum also live on some of the islands of the Lesser Antilles, and our

An opossum using front feet to grasp food.

Virginia opossum has been introduced into some western states but did not occur there naturally.

Didelphis marsupialis, which includes our Virginia opossum, probably has the greatest range of any of the Didelphids, inhabiting parts of Canada southward through the Americas to northern Argentina. The Virginia opossum has extended its range northward hundreds of miles within historic times.

31

Spring

THE LAND is bleak and pale. In the northern United States and southward over a vast area, snow has covered the earth for months. In parts of the south, the time of lean pickings and aching cold has hung on until the countryside looks tired and beaten. Now, though the land may be drab and some of its wild citizens walk with the leanness of winter hunger, there is new life and movement in the fields and forests.

Those cheery fellows that cold seems never to daunt—the chickadees —show a new urgency. Their calls ring out clearer and sharper today. The wind stands from the south, and during the night black specks of northward-migrating warblers briefly flicked their way across the full moon. Deep in last year's tangle of winter-battered grasses tiny green shoots have begun to appear. It is the first faint sign of the green fire that sweeps northward in spring each year.

It is an April day, beautiful and capricious as only such a day can be. Under an abandoned barn, which is gradually crumbling into the rank orchard grasses around it, a mother opossum is nursing her young. The night before she has foraged in a meandering course across the half-dead orchard and through the tangle of vines and shrubs that line the little stream nearby. Her progress, never very fast at best, was much slower than usual, for the babies in her pouch made her travel difficult. She dined on insects, scratched out from beneath rotting logs, and once laboriously scrambled up one of the old apple trees and tested a withered husk of fruit still clinging on a stark branch. A little corn stored in the crib near the old barn filled out her meal. Now she rests on her side as her young nudge her belly while they nurse.

32

The dog-tooth violet, the land snail, and the spring-blooming bloodroot are a part of the opossum's spring world.

The opossum's nest under the old barn is ideal for such weather. She has gathered leaves and grass and made a warm retreat, safe from the wind and out of the way of most enemies. She has been using this nest for some months, though most of her kind are nomads, seldom staying long in any one place.

The location of the old barn is good, too. For an opossum, it has almost everything that is necessary. Not far away is the small stream, with its wooded banks and decaying tree limbs and logs. The old orchard is a bountiful place, providing apples in the fall, which the opossum dearly loves. At the end of the orchard a brushy fencerow has

A fallen tree is a good place for beetles, a favored food.

edged in. A growth of young persimmon trees furnishes the most delectable fruits of all, and they persist on the tree into early winter. Beyond this is a cornfield that filled the old corn crib with the golden grain that has been the opossum's staple food during the long, cold months.

Two things adjacent to each other provide ideal opossum habitat: woods and water. Opossums seem to prefer small streams, although they will also live near ponds or even larger bodies of water. And woods, preferably open woods, and especially those with old hollow

34

den trees, seem to be most sought after as homes. Modern agriculture, which has created an interspersion of crop fields and woody draws or stream hollows, has favored the spread and increase of the opossum.

The opossum differs from many animals in that it is not especially territorial and seems to have no firmly fixed home range. "Territory," to the student of wildlife, means an area that an animal claims and defends against others of its own kind. Thus a pair of nesting mallards select a certain part of the swamp where they will loaf and feed, and drive away other mallards that attempt to use the same spot. Foxes or coyotes usually have a small area near their dens that they defend from others of their kind.

Searching around a rotting log for insects and worms.

(Top) Litter of opossums
in tree root.

(Bottom) Opossum drink-
ing from a stream.

Up a tree for persimmons, a preferred fall and winter food.

The World of the Opossum

The "home range" of an animal is usually larger than its territory. A home range is the area over which it forages for food, which may be a few acres of ground for the cottontail rabbit, or an area thirty miles in diameter for a coyote. When animal populations are high, several home ranges may overlap.

Most opossums wander from place to place, often not even using the same den two nights in a row, but a few individuals may live out their entire lives in an area of only forty acres. None, however, are territorial, which would mean displaying some belligerence in order to defend their territories. Nor are they especially sociable. Most opossums are loners, once they leave their mothers, and they almost never associate closely except to mate. Severe weather, where dens are scant, may possibly offset this solitary behavior; occasionally several opossums have been found in a single den, though they were all of the same sex. But even when two opossums use the same den, they go their separate ways when foraging for food.

Snow-covered river bottom land is habitat for deer and opossum.

The opossum rarely goes far from a stream or other water.

On a mild February night, as she foraged for food along the little stream, the mother opossum met a male opossum making his rounds. There was an interval of sniffing, punctuated by low growls from the male and a peculiar clicking sound. Perhaps this clicking functions as a sexual stimulant, since it is one of the sounds opossums commonly make during breeding season. But other factors within the animals themselves, unknown to us in any detail, had already been at work, and the two came together in a brief sexual union and immediately parted company, the male possibly going on to meet his destiny under the wheels of a speeding automobile, the female to her old barn nest. From this encounter has resulted the ten babies busily nursing within the mother opossum's pouch.

Mating of opossums has caused much speculation by rural people. One of the most obvious oddities they soon discover, upon dissecting a male opossum, is its forked penis. Actually, the male has a forked glans, which wouldn't seem so odd if the vaginal cavity of the female

39

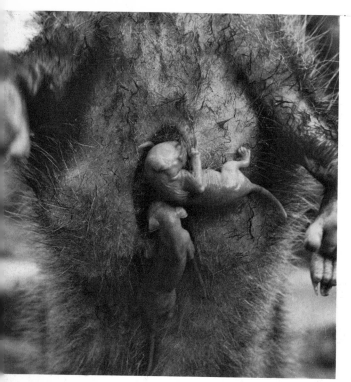 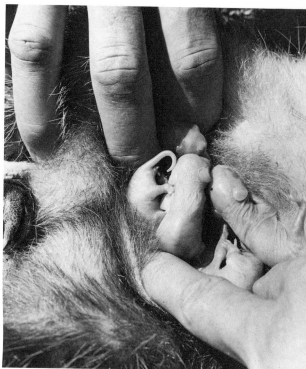

View of young opossums.   *Thirty-day-old young in pouch.*

was as easily seen as the male's penis: it's forked, too, and readily accommodates the forked glans.

But the human imagination is fanciful. Not knowing the female's vaginal structure, some early pioneer, searching for a double opening, decided that opossums must copulate through the nose and then, after a suitable time, the female must sneeze the young into her pouch!

This old idea is still current. As information officer for the Missouri Department of Conservation, I often get letters asking me to confirm or deny this, usually to settle a bet. The sex habits of our wild creatures are little known to most of us and not completely known to professional zoologists. Thus false ideas continue to flourish.

At this stage the pouch is crowded.

Sixty days old, still attached to the nipple.

Actually, our unknown pioneer who first proposed this odd way of opossum breeding was at least exhibiting a scientific inquiry and hypothesis. The trouble is, not all people observe phenomena the same way—some people are trained to *see* better than others and to look a little deeper.

Opossums produce offspring just about the same way any other mammal does, though they do it a great deal faster. In fact, so quickly do female opossums give birth after conception that their offspring have been called "veritable abortions." The average number of fertile eggs in a female at mating time is twenty-two. Usually, not all of these are fertilized, though it happens occasionally. When it does, tragedy strikes,

Still firmly attached, though there is no longer room enough within the pouch.

for the female has only thirteen teats, one for each baby, and any excess offspring must necessarily perish.

After mating the spermatozoa find their way to the eggs lying dormant in the female's ovaries, above the bifurcate uterus. Each egg fertilized admits one sperm, then begins forming albumin and the egg membrane. An opossum egg is similar to most other eggs except for the hard outer shell. It is larger than the human egg—measuring about one thirty-second of an inch in diameter—and is composed of shell membrane, egg white or albumin, and yolk. The yolk is about the same size as the entire human egg. The opossum egg, unlike the hen's, does not contain enough food material to nourish the embryo, so it must be nourished from the mother. This is true in all the higher mammals.

At fertilization, the egg, which has eleven chromosomes, receives an additional eleven chromosomes from the sperm and now has the full opossum complement of twenty-two. The egg soon begins its journey from the ovary to the uterus, although the opossum lacks the elaborate

42

placenta, or afterbirth, to nourish the embryo. For this reason things happen swiftly and birth is hastened.

Carl G. Hartman, who probably knows more about opossums than anyone else, has described development as follows:

First there is the naked ovum or yolk as it comes from the ovary. Within twenty-four hours it becomes covered with albumen and the shell membrane. At the end of the seven-day period the egg has reached the stage of a hollow vesicle lined with three cell layers. In this there is, as yet, only a tiny rudiment of the embryo present, although half of the intra-uterine life has already passed. In six more days the embryos have to be ready for birth and their precarious trip to the pouch. The transition from a delicate vesicle smaller than a pinhead to newborn opossum requires only six days. From these data we may calculate the total period of gestation from mating to birth at just about twelve days and eighteen hours.

This is an astounding feat, and one unique on our continent. From the time a baby opossum is conceived until it develops into a creature with air-filled lungs and a functioning digestive tract and neuro-muscular system, less than thirteen days elapse. By contrast, a human infant's lungs do not fill with air until 270 days after conception.

These offspring, born so suddenly into the world, are so tiny that an entire litter of twenty individuals could fit into a teaspoon. But by adulthood the opossum will weigh 28,000 times its weight at birth. A human adult averages 20 times his birth weight.

In Missouri, studies have shown that the average litter of opossums is eight or nine. Similar studies made elsewhere seem to show litters of about the same size. Harold C. Reynolds, in his studies in Missouri, found the smallest litter in wild-trapped females was five young; the largest, thirteen.

Breeding season for opossums varies from north to south, with some breeding in the Deep South starting as early as December. In Texas the peak is in the third week of January. In Missouri it is about the middle of February. Should a female fail to find a mate when her eggs are fertile, she will again be fertile within twenty-eight days. The male is capable of fertile mating at any time of year, but the female is "in heat," or estrus, only at twenty-eight day-intervals during the breeding season.

On the thirteenth day after mating, the female opossum begins to show the familiar signs of giving birth. She is restless as the contractions of the uterus begin. Previous to the actual birth she has been licking and cleaning the interior of the pouch. It is believed that this behavior is due to the swollen teats; licking them may give the animal some comfort. Our pioneer observers, witnessing this behavior, erroneously guessed that the opossum was sneezing the young from her nose into the pouch!

Now, strange as it may seem, although men and opossums have been acquainted since at least A.D. 1500, it was not until 1847 that anyone actually witnessed the birth of an opossum. Dr. Middleton Michel was that man, and he described it as follows:*

The pregnant female was found standing on her hind legs; her body was much bent, and propped up against the corner of the cage; her muzzle in immediate contact with the cloacal opening, which was red, tumefied and distended; a young appeared at the opening, and was conveyed by the mother's mouth to the pouch, or, perhaps licked in, as her tongue seemed busily employed within, and around and about the pouch.

Dr. Michel missed the actual migration of the young into the pouch, though he did witness marsupial birth for the first time. The young are not "conveyed into the pouch" by the mother's mouth, nor are they licked in. These thirteen-day-old embryos, without any assistance from the mother other than to be licked free of their chorionic fluid, immediately crawl a distance of at least three inches, over the mother's body surface, and enter the pouch. Even then their journey is not over; they

* From *Possums,* by Carl G. Hartman, University of Texas Press, Austin, 1952.

44

must seek and find the nipple of a teat—scarcely larger than the head of a pin—and attach themselves to it.

Such a journey was first actually witnessed by Carl G. Hartman and his wife in 1920. Since that time it has been seen several times, most notably by Harold C. Reynolds, who observed the birth of two entire litters and even clocked the time required with the aid of a stop watch.

Licking the pouch and the vicinity of the vulva must help create conditions favorable to such a journey. Observations on the birth of both opossums and kangaroos seem to show that the licking of the vulva, belly, and pouch has a useful purpose in aiding the young to find their way there. Young opossums placed on the dry fur of their mother are not able to climb as easily as they can when either they or the hair is slicked down by wetting. Young have been observed to recoil from the prickly dry hair when they deviated from their proper course. Certainly the licking of the embryos as they emerge is vital, for if this is not done the young—held prisoner by the surface tension of their watery sheath—will die. They are too tiny to break their own way free of the chorionic fluid. Nearly all female mammals perform this ritual at birth.

Once having proved that the embryos are not "sneezed" into the pouch or transferred from vulva to pouch by the mother's mouth, scientists were faced with an even greater mystery: how do the young know enough to crawl to the pouch and attach themselves to a life-giving teat? Instinct is the easy answer, though this is really no answer at all but a mask for our lack of knowledge.

Eventually it was noted that the position of the mother—semi-upright—must be one factor, for the young appear to climb upward in all circumstances. If they will move in an up direction at all events, the pouch necessarily lies in their path. The term applied to the action was "negative geotropism," which means a tendency to go away from the pull of gravity. In the light of this theory, everything seemed to fit quite neatly until someone discovered that the embryos have no functional inner ear at all, and that without this they cannot record gravitational pull. This function does not begin until the forty-first day of life.

Once "negative geotropism" was ruled out as an explanation for the tiny opossum's tendency to crawl ever upward, scientists looked for some other explanation. It had been demonstrated that young opossums, pulled away from the teats and placed on the mother's belly, would invariably travel upward, whichever way the skin was tilted—even if it meant moving *away* from the pouch. There could be no doubt that the tiny creature was not blindly seeking the pouch; it was just responding to some mysterious force that moved it in an upward direction.

The "mysterious force" actually wasn't mysterious at all. Close observation and a little applied common sense supplied the answer to why the opossum crawled upward, if it did not answer *why* it crawled at all. The tiny opossum, when just born, is provided with fairly well developed front legs with strong claws. The rest of the creature tapers away to hind limbs that are mere undeveloped five-lobed pads. The only means of locomotion are the front legs, the rest of the body simply being dragged. Given the impulse to crawl, as the opossum certainly is, and with only the front legs working, the natural thing is for the rest of the body to fall with the force of gravity. Thus the front of the animal is always pointed up, and that's the way it travels. On a strictly level surface the crawling would be aimless, but the mother opossum's posture for birth—a half-sitting position—presents a rising surface to the young as it emerges from the birth opening. The pouch lies in its path, although undoubtedly an occasional young one must miss the pouch and perish.

We do not yet know *why* the baby opossum is driven to move blindly, even though we know *how* it crawls upward. It does not do this voluntarily, having no brain for voluntary activity at this stage of life. We can merely dub such movements reflex actions and thus cover another gap in our knowledge of this mysterious thing we call life.

Seventy days old.

We know only this: a sufficient number of opossum young climb to the pouch and find a teat to not only keep opossum numbers up but to actually populate new range. With the average litter about eight or nine, and when you consider that opossums raise two litters a year (some writers believe that for a few there may be three litters), it is not surprising that opossums manage to fill all their suitable range. The opossum needs plenty of replacements, because accidents befall it at every turn and death is common in the wild.

Once in the pouch, the young manage to find a teat in what must seem a forest of hair. For many years students of the wild knew opossum young only after discovering them in the pouch and, never seeing them unattached from a teat, concluded that they must have grown there. Still others believed the young were everted from inside the female's belly, attached to the teat.

47

The World of the Opossum

The newborn opossum's face is reminiscent of a frog's. It has a fairly wide mouth and strong facial muscles, features well adapted for sucking. Its clawed forelimbs get it to the pouch, where the grasping mouth finds the tiny nipple. It begins to nurse immediately, the nipple providing both nourishment and a tether on which it will remain for some time. The claws are deciduous: that is, they drop off after they have served their function, in the same way the egg tooth of a chick drops off once it has served its purpose. The claws would be a liability in the close confines of the pouch.

The mother's nipples gradually elongate as the young nurse, permitting them a certain amount of movement within the pouch. I've startled an old female lazing out of her nest with young sprawled outside her relaxed pouch and have seen her run into the nest box, dragging the young, still attached. This same sort of thing has been seen in mice and rats, the young bumping along on their backs—but not relinquishing that precious nipple—when their mother flees from some danger.

The young remain attached to the nipple for about sixty days, long enough to have developed some teeth that could cause a problem. They do not, for the baby opossum's milk teeth do not develop in the center, but at the sides. Thus the long attachment has no damaging effect on the teeth—or on the mother!

At this stage of life, the opossum is not yet a homoiotherm, or what is incorrectly called a "warm-blooded animal." This term refers to an animal with heat-regulating powers to keep the body temperature fairly constant, no matter what the temperature of its surroundings may be. Most mammals have a uniform body temperature, although heat-regulating mechanisms are often not completely functional early in life. And in hibernating animals the mechanism is not completely functional when the animal is in its torpid state. Uniform body temperature is desirable, because "cold-blooded animals"*—snakes, frogs, and toads

* The so-called "cold-blooded animals" are in scientific terminology called *poikilotherms.*—The Editor.

48

for example—whose body temperatures vary with the surrounding medium, cannot perform their usual life functions if temperatures fall. The drop in their own body temperatures forces them into a temporary torpor or, if cold weather persists, into hibernation. The baby opossum is an incomplete homoiotherm and needs the warmth of its mother to keep it active. The pouch supplies not only food but warmth.

In the middle of the nineteenth century it was believed that baby opossums were too weak to suck and that the mother pumped milk into them. This is not true. The baby opossum works for its dinner, like all other mammals. (Neither is it true that baby opossums grow onto the nipple. They are sometimes difficult to loosen, but gentle tugging can do the trick.)

It is sometimes claimed that the elongated nipple extends down into the baby's stomach, since how else could it remain attached, suck, and breathe, all at the same time? Surely it would choke if it tried to do all these things simultaneously. Not so. The baby opossum has an unusual arrangement of the epiglottis that prevents choking. This lid to the larynx, which closes the glottis (the opening to the air passages), is tubular and extends up into the nasal chamber in such a way that milk may run down into the stomach without obstructing air passage.

It is interesting to speculate on the atmosphere of the pouch in which the young must live during their first months of life. The babies must breathe and rebreathe air which, in the confines of the pouch, contains up to twenty times the normal content of carbon dioxide. Scientists have wondered if this heavy carbon dioxide concentration serves some useful, unknown role or if it merely demonstrates an unusual tolerance on the part of the opossum. In human beings, a rise in the carbon dioxide content of the air causes an increased rate and depth of respiration. Life in an atmosphere such as that in the pouch would seem to be intolerable to us, but some authorities believe it may actually be beneficial to the baby opossums.

49

The World of the Opossum

On this early spring day the ten baby opossums nursing within the pouch are unaware of the many pitfalls they have escaped thus far. Since the February night almost two months ago when they were conceived, they have developed from tiny eggs, been born, and managed the perilous journey from birthplace to pouch. At forty days of age they can, if removed from their mother, stand erect, walk a few steps, and even cry when disturbed. They have come a long way on the journey of life in a remarkably short time. The perils they have passed are only a small portion of what lies ahead, for life in the wild is never kind.

White-tailed deer trotting through opossum country.

Summer

SUMMER IN OPOSSUM COUNTRY is a pleasant time. Hot days and warm nights are a welcome change from the biting winds of winter and the fickle, tantalizing promise of spring. Summer is the time of growth and fullness. It is a time when plant life is burgeoning and so is most animal life. Living is not always so easy.

Late winter and early spring are usually the most trying seasons for wild creatures. It is then that foods for many of them are at their lowest ebb. Vegetation that might afford shelter from the weather and from enemies is winter-battered and sparse. The multitude of wild animals that were born the previous spring perish in numbers that would astound most people if only they knew. Such species as quail and rabbits, especially, are cut back in nature's winnowing process by as much as 80 per cent, succumbing to cold, starvation, sickness, and predation.

The opossums, too, have suffered considerably through the winter and early spring. But now they wax fat on the earth's summer bounty and increase their numbers. By midsummer many female opossums are carrying a second litter of young in their pouches. Some authorities think there may be a third litter, at least in the deep South, but two litters a year is certainly the rule.

In Missouri breeding begins in February, with most litters born near the end of that month. Allowing 80 to 90 days from birth to weaning, and a gestation period of 12½ days, a second litter could not be weaned until mid-to-late August. Thus there would be no time for rearing a third litter before cold weather. Harold C. Reynolds, working in Missouri, found evidence that not all females mate even a second time.

Development of the young within the pouch is rapid, though not

51

nearly so fast as the amazing 12½-day development in the uterus. When born, baby opossums are less than half an inch long and so small that it would take 175 of them to make an ounce. Growth in various litters of young is approximately equal for the first thirty days, then differences begin to appear. Such variations in growth rates probably are due to the physical condition of the mothers and the amount and type of foods they consume.

The tiny babies at birth can climb blindly to the pouch and attach themselves to a nipple but do little else. By the seventeenth day the hind legs and tail are becoming functional and the sexes can begin to be distinguished; until this time the hind legs and tail of the body have been relatively undeveloped. Development then speeds up for the hinder parts. By the thirty-sixth day vibrissae, or whiskers, are beginning to grow around the mouth. Body hair begins to be seen on the back about the forty-third day.

By the sixty-fourth day the mouth and eyes are open and the young are able to leave the mother's pouch. They do this usually when she is asleep during the day, groping tentatively at the world nearby. It is an amusing sight to watch the ratlike young with their bulging black eyes, whiskers aquiver, as they crawl fumblingly around their sleeping mother. At first they seldom venture more than a few inches away from her warm body, but as the days go by they become more venturesome.

Caged opossums that I had would wander in and out between the bars—only the finest mesh wire would hold the tiny fellows—and clamber up the cage side. I kept one mother opossum and her babies in my youngsters' playhouse; they would occasionally slip down a knothole in the floor and be lost, temporarily. When we would take the young away from the mother they would seem to be seeking her and would make a peculiar sneezing sound which I thought might be a call.

The teats of the mother are by now greatly elongated, and the young opossums loll outside the pouch on hot summer days, still firmly attached and nursing. By their seventy-first day the young can control

52

Exploring fallen tree for grubs and insects.

their body temperature somewhat, though before this they are unable to do so. They wander away from the mother for short distances but return to the mammae for food. By their seventy-eighth day they have teeth sufficiently developed to chew and eat small portions of solid food, and by the eightieth to ninetieth day they complete their full set of 50 teeth and are weaned. Now they are smaller editions of their parents.

Mother opossums can control the opening of the pouch and permit the young to enter and leave as necessary. On hot summer days they relax the pouch muscles and allow the young ones to sun. As the young develop they get to be quite a pocketful, and eventually their size is such that not all of them can get back into the pouch at one time. The young clutch the mother's fur and ride on her back when she goes on her nightly wanderings. If she has to take to the water when carrying

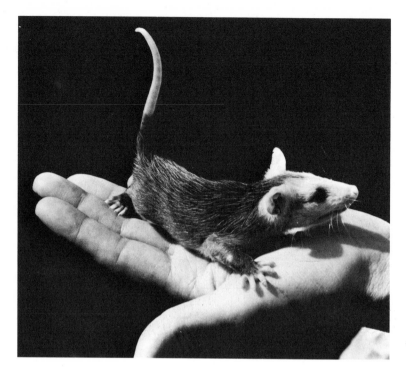

Approximately seventy-five days old. At this stage they only want to return to the mother.

pouched young, she can close the mouth of the pouch to protect her babies.

The mother opossum is a good mother, keeping the pouch clean and seemingly possessed of inexhaustible patience. I can't imagine a human mother putting up with such a squirming mass of youngsters, hanging on her back when she goes to the store, or crawling all over her in short exploratory journeys when she tries to nap. Yet I have never seen a female opossum exhibit any special sign of impatience and, while she doesn't seem to instruct her young in correct behavior, I've never seen one chastise her young for any actions, either.

The opossum has a number of traits that make it adaptable as a species to its environment. The chief thing in its favor is that it is a rather unspecialized animal, without any critical needs that can be met in one situation only. Unlike, say, trout, which can live only in water of a few degrees' variation in temperature, the opossum can tolerate extremes of temperature. A relative of the opossum, the winsome koala of Australia, is so specialized that it can feed only on eucalyptus leaves, whereas the opossum can eat almost anything.

In order for a species to survive it must be adaptable, and the history of the earth is replete with tales of animals and plants that became so specialized in their habits that they perished when conditions changed. The more "generalized" an animal is, the greater its chances of surviving as a species, whatever changes may occur. Man was, and is, a rather generalized type, able to meet successfully a great variety of challenges of environment. He also has the ability to alter his immediate environment in his favor and has been able to survive from the hottest, driest

Traveling with the mother—age eighty days.

Quite a load to climb with.

deserts to the coldest and most rugged climes on earth.

The opossum makes no special demands on its environment. It gets along by being able to eat almost anything (omnivorous in its feeding), is able to endure many kinds of weather, but will also seek a den for protection from the severest weather.

The opossum's prime range is woods and waters, and it is also a good swimmer, as we might suspect from its preference for a habitat close to streams. Harold C. Reynolds reported that opossums swam with ease and occasionally took to the water to escape capture. If an opossum was frightened when swimming, it often surface dived and swam short distances under water. He reported that when in danger opossums have been known to swim small bodies of water and lie with only the nose exposed in the shallow water of the opposite shore.

J. Kenneth Doutt reported on three experiments he conducted to test opossum swimming ability. He found that they swim with ease and considerable force. They evidenced no fear of water and would dive and swim underwater. He found they could not stand cold water for any extended period of time and believed that large bodies of cold water would be an effective barrier to opossums.

Doutt found that opossums swam in different ways—"dog fashion," "pacing," (i.e., with both legs on the same side moving in unison), with a walking action, and also with front feet and then rear feet moving

As the young opossums mature they sometimes make short ventures away from the den.

A fairly typical opossum family, the young appear almost adult now and about ready to go on their own.

together. The toes were extended in swimming, and his opossums uttered peculiar noises, "sort of a whine, almost a purr," as he described it.

In 1928 Ernest Thompson Seton delineated the opossum's range as from southern New York State, across Pennsylvania, Ohio, and Indiana (just barely intruding into southern Michigan), Illinois, southeastern Iowa, all of Missouri, eastern Kansas, and all of Oklahoma except the panhandle, down through mid-Texas to the Mexican border. In 1941 Harold C. Reynolds showed the range had extended from 200 to 400 miles westward and from 100 to 150 miles northward. In thirteen years the opossum had apparently spread its range considerably.

Besides this west and north extension of their range, opossums were introduced into central California, where they found conditions there so hospitable that they rapidly spread all along the western half of that state, from north of San Francisco to Baja California. In 1959 Charles and Elizabeth Schwartz reported that the opossum had spread completely up and down the west coast, penetrating well inland in Oregon and Washington. Recent reports also confirm the establishment of the opossum in parts of Arizona.

All these extreme western populations result almost certainly from initial stockings by man, but how do we explain the extremely rapid spread of the range in only a few decades in the eastern United States? Reynolds believed that certain uses of the land were probable contributory factors. The great upsurge in building farm ponds and water

Badgers dig burrows sometimes used by opossums.

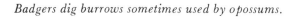

reservoirs following the drought years made it possible for opossums to enter and inhabit regions where formerly they could not live because of a lack of permanent water. Possibly another contributing factor was the killing off of large predators such as coyotes, wolves, foxes, and horned owls, but lack of predation on opossums is probably not as significant a factor as the creation of new habitats.

The opossum does not appear to be too firmly attached to any one place, and is a great rover. In 1942, Daniel W. Lay trapped 117 individuals during a two-year period. Of these, 58 were taken only once, 22 were taken twice, and 31 three or more times. Only three remained in the study area long enough to yield any information as to the size of the home range, and Lay concluded:

The wandering habit may be more pronounced in opossums than in

Opossums readily take to water and prefer to have it near home territory.

The opossum is a good swimmer. Note exposed nose.

some species. . . . The evidence suggests that almost half of the population on a given area are distinctly itinerant. Seasonal food and water changes cause definite movements and may account for some apparent wandering.

As far back as 1872, G. Lincecum reported that opossums were found under the floors of dwelling houses "where they had been for some time and had evidently taken up winter quarters; they did not remain there long, nor do I think they dwell long at any one place." R. E. Hesselschwert put up den boxes in hedgerows in the prairie portion of Illinois, finding that, although opossums built bulky nests of corn shucks and leaves inside the dens, an animal did not use any one box for any length of time.

Reynolds, studying the opossum in Missouri, released sixty-eight marked individuals at two sites. In spite of intensive hunting in an area of one half mile radius around each site, and although many new individuals were captured in this area, only five marked animals were recovered. One of these was recaptured 47 hours after release, approximately a quarter of a mile away, whereas the other was found 58 days later only 510 feet from the point of release. The remaining three were recaptured for the second time between one quarter and one half mile

Lizard lives in opossum country.

away, 24, 63, and 87 days later, respectively.

Reynolds found that opossums were apparently totally removed from his study area by hunting and trapping in December and January. He knew that at least thirty-six animals had lived in the area the previous five months. But from February through June, the area yielded seventeen adult individuals. This rapid influx and the prompt disappearance of all but five of the marked animals and the recapture of one individual a quarter mile away only 47 hours after release, all tend to substantiate the belief that most opossums wander widely and at random and that probably few of them establish a fixed home range. Such wandering, with more favorable habitats being created, must surely account for

A predator of opossums, the bobcat.

*A den of young opossums in
a tree root.*

much of the opossum's spread to the north and west.

The opossum has more teeth than any other American land mammal, 50 being its normal number. By contrast the raccoon has only 40 teeth; coyotes, foxes, and bears, 42; the weasel tribe, 34; bobcats, 28; and man, 32. It's no wonder that the toothy "grin" of the opossum has impressed itself on those describing it: 50 glittering teeth look like formidable armament. Fortunately, the opossum is ordinarily so inoffensive that its many teeth are more intimidating than effectual as weapons, so far as man is concerned.

Most unusual is the large number of incisors—18—found in the opossum. Its dental formula is:

$$\text{I}\,\frac{5}{4}\ \ \text{C}\,\frac{1}{1}\ \ \text{P}\,\frac{3}{3}\ \ \text{M}\,\frac{4}{4}$$

which means there are five incisors on either side of a center line in the upper jaw, with four incisors on each side in the lower jaw, one canine above and below on either side, three premolars, and four molars, both above and below. The numerous teeth are an easy way to identify the opossum's skull from that of any other animal of similar size.

The Schwartzes reported that individual opossums have been found with their upper front teeth worn down to the gums and other teeth abcessed or missing.

Among mammals, the opossum's teeth most closely resemble those of the carnivores, or flesh eaters. They have the same incisors for cutting

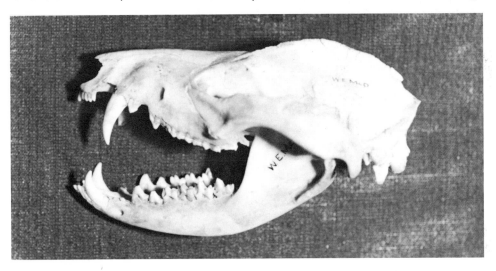

Skull and jaws of opossum showing some of the 50 teeth.

off bites, the canines for tearing, and the molars for grinding a variety of foods. The molars are not as flat as the bear's but rather sharper, like the raccoon's. This similarity of the opossum's teeth to those of the carnivores is reflected in the opossum's food preferences. It likes animal matter best of all, though it will eat a wide variety of things. One report from Michigan indicated that 80 per cent of the opossum's food was of animal origin.

65

That does not necessarily mean that the opossum is very outstanding as a predator, at least where larger animals are concerned. A great deal of its diet is made up of insects such as grasshoppers, crickets, squash and stink bugs, various ground beetles, May beetles, and ants. Most of the flesh food eaten is carrion, with cottontail rabbit heading the list. This carrion-eating trait sometimes brings man's wrath down on the opossum as a chicken-eater. Usually, the opossum is guilty only of eating dead chickens or the remains. There is no doubt, however, that some opossums will raid the poultry yard now and then.

In Maryland, L. M. Llewellyn and F. M. Uhler found that dewberries and blackberries made up almost one fifth of the opossum's total food in June and July. In September and October, persimmons, wild grapes, and apples raised the total to almost one fourth. November showed the highest consumption of plant food (32 per cent) when grapes comprised 15 per cent and pokeberry and persimmon 6 per cent each. Smilax, corn, and apples appeared in small amounts. Opossums ate less plant

Cottontail rabbit hiding in its "form" may be prey of opossum.

Spring peeper, singing in the opossum's world.

food in December (16 per cent), and from January to April only minor occurrences of smilax, corn, and black gum appeared. Other plant foods eaten in minor quantities were beechnuts and the berries of nightshade and ground cherry.

Llewellyn and Uhler found that in Maryland animal food made up 86 per cent of all foods eaten, a third of the yearly diet being insects, with beetles leading. Snails of at least six species were found in the diet, and the opossum ate more millipedes than any other fur animal studied, and crayfishes, spiders, and centipedes were also eaten. Vertebrate animals included wood, meadow, and pine mice, squirrels, and shrews. Birds appeared in the opossums' stomach contents and its droppings on twenty-five occasions. The authors reported:

It is difficult to see how opossums could have taken many of these

67

birds alive, since in most instances they were neither ground-roosting nor ground-nesting species, so it must be assumed that the birds were either sick, injured, or carrion. No bird eggs were noted and only one bobwhite quail was found.

The investigators reported a few frogs, seven snakes, and some salamanders; and fishes also were noted as opossum foods in Maryland.

Earthworms are readily available for the opossum's diet.

Harold C. Reynolds made an intensive study of opossum food habits in Missouri, and his findings generally agree with those of the Maryland study. He noted insects, fruit, some invertebrates other than insects, and

68

Opossum and raccoons inhabit the same kind of range.

mammals, reptiles, cultivated grains and miscellaneous seeds, and birds and eggs in that order of frequency of occurrence. By volume the ranking was: insects, mammals, reptiles, cultivated grains and miscellaneous seeds, fruits, birds and eggs, and invertebrates other than insects. Reynolds examined 259 scats from recently captured opossums over a period from September to May. He also examined stomach contents from animals taken from December through May.

Reynolds found that insect remains occurred most frequently in droppings and also in greatest volume in stomachs examined. They represented at least twenty-five different families of insects, chief of which were the ground beetle, lamellicorn beetle, short-horned grasshopper, squash bug, and stink bug families. It would seem that the opossum's diet preference makes him a valued ally in the fight to control insects.

Oddly enough, insects were found in opossum stomachs in larger amounts during winter than in spring. One would think that during winter insects would be scarce or nonexistent. However, the opossums find them, presumably in hibernation in hollow logs, holes, and other places.

Reynolds stated that the cottontail rabbit was the single most important item of food by volume, in the stomachs of sixty-eight opossums checked. He found twelve mammalian species in all were used as food, with more occurring in winter than at other times. He believed the opossum was not good enough as a predator to have actually caught and eaten most of the animals used as food and believed that the flesh of cottontails, house cats, opossums, squirrels, raccoons, and skunks found was carrion, or animals that had died of other causes. Animals wounded or killed by hunters and not found probably contributed to the opossum's diet, he said.

It is commonly believed that droppings found in the field containing large numbers of persimmon seeds are those of the opossum. Not so, says Reynolds. The opossum seldom swallows the seeds of persimmons, and captive animals fed exclusively on persimmons for an entire week produced only one scat with a single persimmon seed in it.

Contrary to earlier writers' contentions that opossums will readily consume anything edible, Reynolds found that they have a distinct preference for animal matter, particularly for insects. In Missouri, corn is probably the only vegetable matter commonly consumed, other than fruits and berries, and it seems to be eaten only when nothing else is readily available.

Late summer presents the opossum with nearly everything it requires:

insects aplenty and berries and fruits at their most abundant. As summer's growth reaches its zenith and turns down the year toward fruition, mother opossum's second litter of young leave her and strike out on their own. It's a good time to be alive and to make one's way in the world.

The opossum usually spits out persimmon seeds.

Autumn

AUTUMN IS A TIME of reflection for mankind. The days are growing noticeably shorter, and there often is a sharpness in the air. The warm pleasant days of Indian summer that are almost an annual occurrence in opossum country are only a short reprieve before winter cold strikes and snow covers much of its northern range.

Autumn continues to be a time of plenty for the opossum. Nature's granary is full, and he has accumulated a thick layer of fat from his varied diet. Insects that become less troublesome, and therefore less noticeable, to man are still plentifully available to the questing opossum as he makes his nightly rounds.

On the newly bare limbs of the persimmon the golden fruit hangs, ripened to sweetness by the first frosts and delectable to many of nature's creatures—the opossum especially. By day the hunter has picked a pocketful of the sweet fruits, to munch as he follows his searching setter. By night the trees are visited by gray foxes, raccoons, and opossums. With such golden bounty, the wild creatures do not ponder the passing of time, the swift passage of summer into fall and the threat of winter. They take life in its moment and leave reflection to man.

The young have scattered now. The female opossum, no longer burdened with a pouchful of young, moves easily through the autumn nights, searching, rooting, and prying through the moon-dappled countryside for her food. The opossum has a curious habit of poking into everything, possibly out of simple curiosity, more likely in quest of things into which to sink those fifty gleaming teeth. Every nook and cranny is investigated by the animal. One Michigan study of ground

72

Eating insects dug from rotting fallen tree.

dens revealed that opossums might visit any of them in an exploratory way, without actually taking up residence there. Brush piles, horizontal hollow logs, niches and crannies in bluffs, rock piles, and tangles of vines are all probed into. Even houses come in for investigation occasionally, to the consternation of human inhabitants!

Practically every place where opossums live bears their small starlike

73

Opossum using front feet to grasp food.

footprints at some time or other. Shy and secretive by day, at night the opossum roams widely, and the sluggishness exhibited by day becomes feverish activity at night. The animal's walk is flat-footed, the entire sole of the foot touching the ground. On soft mud its front feet leave the characteristic starlike prints, while the monkeylike hind prints show the opposable "thumb" that is one of the animal's distinguishing characteristics. All the toes except the "thumbs" have claws. The rather long toes and opposable "thumb" enable the opossum to climb readily and its prehensile tail aids in climbing. Thus it can reach a great many things that ground-bound animals must pass by. This climbing ability, of course, is related to the opossum's preference for forests or farm woodlands. When pursued by predators the opossum frequently takes to trees to escape the clutching jaws.

In recent times the opossum has readily adapted to semi-city life, and I see them frequently at night in the streets of my home town,

Opossums are good tree climbers and seek lofty branches for safety.

Opossum searches for food at night.

Jefferson City, Missouri. Most people's glimpses of the opossum are in the glare of headlights along highways as opossums feed—sometimes to their own undoing—on traffic-killed animals.

Opossums have a keen sense of smell, and that portion of their brain controlling this function is highly developed. Their keen sense of smell, their eyes that are admirably suited to night vision, plus their sensitive vibrissae help them make their way in the hours of darkness.

If opossums have a keen sense of smell, how about their own odor? Many people are of the opinion that opossums are dirty animals and therefore have an unpleasant odor. Neither notion is true. Opossums are clean creatures, spending a great deal of time in licking and grooming their fur. Most food studies show large quantities of opossum hair in opossum stomachs and in their scats, traceable to the grooming and cleaning of their fur. The idea of opossums being dirty stems, for the most part, from animals held captive under conditions where the opos-

76

sum is not able to keep itself as clean as it normally would.

Most people familiar with opossums find their natural odor accepta-
ble, although some South American opossums have a fetid scent.
Opossums I've kept around for study had a faint musky smell, not at
all unpleasant and nowhere near as noisome as that of foxes, or
skunks and others of the weasel tribe. Neither do opossum scats have
the offensive odor of those foxes, skunks, and other animals.

Along with their other senses that stand them in good stead as they
wander in search of food at night, opossums exhibit a keen sense of
hearing. Just as we are less startled by lightning compared with the
thunder clap, the opossum does not exhibit nervousness to bright light
but will wince at so small a sound as a camera click. Its hearing range
is from 100 to 19,000 cycles per second.

Since they are creatures of the night, admirably adapted to make
their way through the dark hours, opossums may be much more
abundant in an area than one might believe. When we are out during

*Opossum resting and wash-
ing up during night sojourn.*

Startled opossum about to go into the "playing possum" act, or death feint.

the day, the opossum is sleeping in some snug retreat. Often our first inkling of opossums in the neighborhood is when some luckless victim falls prey to our dog, which may drag the lifeless carcass home. Or we may see the opossum scurrying across the street as we arrive home late some evening. Usually, unless we consciously seek him, the opossum goes his way unnoticed by man. The opossum survives as a species, even though beset everywhere by all manner of predators, and crippling and fatal accidents. But it retains its abundance, in spite of high mortality because of its fecundity and not because of its intelligence.

However, one indication that opossums *can* learn simple things and retain them over a period of time was related by Harold C. Reynolds, who had two females in captivity. They were kept for some time in a pen that had a den box with an opening in the side. They quickly learned to use this den box. Later, they were transferred to another pen that had a den box with an opening in the bottom. When they were first placed in the new pen they attempted to enter the den box but, not finding the opening in the usual place, remained outside until the following night, when they discovered the new opening.

After a two-week period they were returned to the original cage. They ran to the den box at the point where they had become accustomed to finding the bottom entrance but, discovering no opening, immediately climbed to the formerly used entrance at the side and entered the box. This surely indicated some retention of knowledge, or memory.

Captive opossums eventually learn to tolerate people but I've never seen any evidence that they recognize or differentiate between human beings, which would be some sort of learning. At first every movement or gesture near them seems menacing, and they exhibit fright or wariness. But they soon learn to endure a certain amount of handling, though you can never be sure they won't attempt to bite, and they never completely abandon being wary at any human movement.

Opossums' behavior when they think they are threatened is always unpredictable. They may attempt to run, they may growl, hiss, or bluff, or they may simply faint away in the "playing dead" reaction. No one can predict exactly what an opossum will do in a stressful situation: it depends on the individual opossum and the situation as he responds to it.

Visualize a robust old male opossum as he leaves his den on a warm autumn evening. He has lain curled up and dozing throughout the sunny hours and early evening. Now it is black night. Just how he knew it was night as he lazed in his dark hole is unknown—possibly hunger pangs stirred him—but now he leaves his burrow entrance. He has paused at the entrance, sampling the outside world, before stepping out, every sense alert. His delicate vibrissae quiver as he scents the air for an odor that might mean an enemy. His beady black eyes search the darkness for any telltale movement. Nothing. So he first makes his way to the small stream that is never far from an opossum's chosen home.

79

The World of the Opossum

On the way he is suddenly confronted with another opossum. He stops, stands his ground, and opens his mouth, revealing his sharp white teeth and dripping saliva. He gives a low hiss. The other opossum pauses momentarily, opens its own mouth, and then ambles off. The old male watches him go and then proceeds toward the stream. This is one reaction to a stressful situation.

Not fast, a cornered opossum seeks any bit of cover that is available.

Playing possum.

Suppose that the animal confronting him had been a vigorous terrier from the nearby farmhouse, out on an autumn evening's romp. The dog would be sniffing here and there, his sense of smell made keener by the slight nip in the air. Suddenly he scents the opossum, at the same time that the old male opossum scents him. This time the old male turns and puts on a burst of speed. His ordinary shambling gait quickens to a trot, then to a rush. Opossums can move with deceptive speed when they need to.

The terrier yaps excitedly and runs after the opossum, just disap-

Opossum feigning death.

pearing toward a thicket. Too late, for inside the thicket is a small wild plum tree. The opossum quickly scampers up to the first stout branches. There it stretches out to patiently outwait the dog. The dog soon tires of such unresponsive game in the branches out of reach and leaves because it has other scents to test this night.

But let's suppose the opossum didn't quite make it to the thicket before the terrier was upon him. Now he has two choices: he can fight or he can "play possum." Exactly what he'll do under the circumstances depends on his past experiences and what effects they have had on him. Since opossums are so unaggressive, if he does elect to fight it will ordinarily be nothing more than as a trapped rat, snapping back at each sally the dog makes and seeking to escape at every opportunity. More

When molested, opossums play dead.

than likely, if all escape seems barred, he will go into the catatonic state that we call "playing possum."

This "playing possum" is puzzling. My experience with it is quite limited because I have not found that specimens I've handled go into this comalike state very readily. Only on rare occasions have I actually seen opossums "playing possum." Not all of them go into this death-feigning state, while some go into it less readily than others. Among captives, the readiness to "play possum" declines as they get used to intruders.

The term "playing possum" is commonly used to cover a great many trancelike states exhibited by many different kinds of animals when in fear or under stress. For some reason the opossum's use of this feint seems to have caught the public fancy, although I'm not convinced the opossum is necessarily the star performer. Going dead, playing dead, thanatosis, letisimulation, akinesia, *Starrkrampfreflex,* tonic immobility, *mortuum simulit,* counterfeiting death, freezing, or "layin' low and sayin' nuffin" are all various terms and phrases describing the opossum's and other animals' reaction to stressful situations. These are all words, merely words, and the mystery that lies behind them remains to be unraveled.

William S. Wiedorn, writing in *Science,* in clinical detail described this unusual state as follows:*

Exposure of the opossum to a threatening stressful situation initiates the following sequence, in which all the components are present to a greater or lesser degree, depending upon the individual animal and its previous experience. First there is exaggerated, if not inefficient, somatic muscular action in an attempt to escape, with some of the animals making a low growling sound and snapping. This initial and not invariably present phase of hyperactivity is marked by a rapid heart rate, increased rate and depth of respiration, defecation, occasionally urination, extrusion of a foul-smelling yellow-green material in a fine spray from the perianal region, periorbital muscle tension, and a drawing

*Copyright 1964 by the American Association for the Advancement of Science.

Opossums seem to enjoy just ambling around in shallow water.

back of the angles of the mouth. The initial hyperactive phase is of short duration, from a few seconds to five to ten minutes. This hyperactive phase is often so transitory as to be almost absent.

In the second or catatonic phase, the animal becomes semirigid and usually assumes a posture on one side with the limbs partially extended, the mouth open, and the tongue slightly protruded. The limbs may be flaccid or rigid at various times while the animal is in this catatonic-like state. The heart rate is decreased and the apical pulse is often impalpable. The respiratory movements are slowed and predominantly abdominal. Frequently they are so slight that the abdominal and thoracic movements cannot be detected. Following periods of stimulation or stress, while in the catatonic state, the opossum may exhibit periods of apnea for 30 seconds or more. [Apnea is transitory cessation of breathing.] There is greatly increased salivation, with a pool of watery saliva forming about the animal's mouth. The mucuous membranes become pale and dry. The animal may continue to defecate while in this state, each succeeding stool becoming more watery. The tendon reflexes are usually absent, as is sometimes the corneal reflex. The cremasteric reflex has invariably been present. In the latter part of the initial hyperactive phase and the early part of the retarded catatonic phase, the eyes may show rapid lateral nystagmoid movements [a movement of the eyeballs from side to side]; the limbs may show a rapid and gross tremor, most marked in the hind limbs. If held up by the skin of the dorsum of the neck during this period, the animal assumes a posture with the mouth agape, the tongue protruded, the forepaws clenched together, and the hind limbs extended laterally with gross muscle tremors. The eyes do not close, although the lids may move close together. During the catatonic-like state, the animals do not respond to painful forced flexion of the fingers, rough bodily manipulation, tactile stimulation, irritation of the nasal vibrissae, and stroking of the cornea.

Probably no one else has described "playing possum" so clinically. In brief, the opossum first seems to be trying to escape and may lose control over its bowels in so doing. It's heart and breathing rate are rapid during this phase. It then more or less suddenly goes into a trance-

86

like state, with heart and breathing rate seemingly almost absent, and to all appearances is dead. While in this trance it does not respond to having its toes bent painfully, to pulling of its whiskers, or even to touching the eyeballs.

Such behavior at first seems baffling to us, for it obviously isn't anything the opossum can control, coming on with dramatic suddenness from within. Fear or threats or rough handling can induce the state in many opossums, but its exact causes remain a mystery.

But "freezing" into immobility, or being hypnotized, are not confined to the opossum. All of us have seen people start to cross the street and suddenly be confronted with a car bearing down on them. Most people jump nimbly out of the way, but how often have you seen someone freeze, unable to move either forward or backward? Psychiatrists tell us different people react differently to the same situation: those who freeze may be exhibiting a behavior somewhat akin to the opossum's.

The opossum's death feigning is not acting. It is not a consciously directed thing but seems to be brought about by an outer stimulus that triggers some sort of reaction within the animal itself. The animal can no more stop the involuntary action than a sensitive plant can withhold the folding of its leaves. Nor is the opossum alone in its death feigning. Other observers have noted behavior remarkably similar in foxes, various birds, reptiles, and other creatures, down to insects. Most of us, at one time or another, have put toads, frogs, or lizards "to sleep" by holding them between our two palms and suddenly inverting them. Maybe we also softly stroked the belly as we slowly withdrew one hand. The creature would lie there for some minutes, seemingly hypnotized.

This type of behavior reminds me of a response in birds that may be related to that of "death feigning." It is the "freezing" of baby quail and ducklings when warned by the hen of nearby danger. Occasionally a hunter will be able to pick up the immobile walnut-sized quail chick, so firmly is its obedience to the mother (and perhaps some inner mechanism?) imbued in it. In these examples, though, the immobility

87

is not so deep and the creature can terminate it at will. Not so with the opossum. Here is the clinical description by Wiedorn of the opossum's return from his trance.

At any time, depending upon as yet unknown intraorganismic factors, the opossum may suddenly reintegrate and make attempts to escape. This is most likely if the animal is suddenly exposed to a new and major stimulus. The opossum may also gradually reintegrate when placed back in the safety of its cage, but diminished awareness may persist for an hour or more.

The animals may remain in the catatonic-like state for as long as two to six hours, or only for several minutes. In their cages the opossums may show immobility in an abnormal position for many hours after being stressed. This state may even be induced repeatedly in the same animal on the same day, with longer or shorter periods of catatonia. However, the opossum becomes less likely to exhibit the catatonic-like response as it gains experience with either a particular stress situation or a particular experimenter.

Wiedorn was interested in the opossum from a psychiatric standpoint, believing that it made an especially useful animal for study since its "playing possum" exhibited a catatoniclike syndrome, illustrating all the same effects shown in men in psychopathological situations.

The wide difference that opossums may exhibit in death feigning is described by two Kansas investigators, Henry S. Fitch and Lewis L. Sandidge, who were live-trapping and marking opossums.

Feigning was especially frequent in response to clipping of toes and ears when the animal was marked. In some that were handled, the feigning reaction was weak or incomplete, the animal arising almost immediately after collapsing or beginning to collapse in the feint.

Those that feigned death usually maintained the deception for not more than two or three minutes after a person had moved away out of sight. The opossum first raised its head and sniffed, listened, and looked about cautiously for a short time, with body and limbs still relaxed in the feigning posture. Failing to detect any sign of danger, it gradually shifted to a sitting position, and then to a standing one, from which it

88

began to move away with many short pauses at first, and then more rapidly.

This differs somewhat from Wiedorn's description of "playing possum." Fitch and Sandidge were handling a variety of opossums, of all ages, sexes, and experiences, and their behavior varied from aggressive hostility to almost complete passivity, with only a few of the animals exhibiting death feigning and even these exhibiting it sometimes in an incomplete manner.

The opossum apparently cannot control when or how it will come out of its trance. Some individuals wake up ready to run, but others take quite a bit of time before readjusting to their regular behavior

Red fox, eating rabbit, sometimes preys on opossum.

patterns. It depends on the animal and the situation.

Surely such behavior must have some sort of survival value, contributing to the success of the opossum as a species. A great many predators or natural enemies of the opossum will not waste time on an apparently dead carcass. If the opossum was seized by the terrier and shaken and flung to the ground, to lie there immobile and seemingly dead, it is likely the terrier would give it another shake or two and then go its way. The opossum would lie there for a time and then slowly get up, proceed to the brook to wash and groom its fur, and then continue its nightly prowl.

Since many predators want moving prey, the ancestral opossums that went into a state of immobile shock, from fright or rough handling, might have been the ones that survived noctural clashes with ancient predators. They would have passed on this valuable characteristic to their offspring, and the race would have survived by "playing dead."

When one considers the opossum's lack of aggressiveness, its comparatively slow speed, and its lack of natural defenses, it is a wonder it has lived as a species as long as it has. As Seton pointed out, most animals that are good to eat have some natural defense: the speed and good vision and hearing of the rabbit; the fighting ferocity of the weasel; the armor of the armadillo; the sharp barbs of the porcupine, and the "poison gas" of the skunk.

Possibly the chief foe of the opossum today is the domestic dog. Throughout much of the opossum's range, but especially in the South, free-running dogs are common. In rural areas it is common to keep several dogs for fox and raccoon hunting, and these dogs, if not penned or chained, can be abroad at all hours. They frequently constitute a menace to all wildlife and are especially vicious in chasing deer. In my home state of Missouri there are areas where hounds have harried deer so much that they were driven out, and what should be prime deer range supports scarcely any of the animals. One can only guess at the other, smaller wild creatures that are killed or tormented by such dogs.

90

The opossum must suffer considerably from their onslaughts.

Man is a predator, too, for he hunts the opossum for food and sport, although possibly less so today than formerly. In rural areas many people consider the opossum a "varmint" to be killed on sight, just on the chance that it might be a chicken thief. Besides man, the foxes, coyotes, bobcats, and especially the great horned owls prey on the opossum; the owl, whose hunting hours coincide with the opossum's, pounces on it and kills it with ease.

The opossum's world, like that of most wild creatures, is one of possible danger on every hand. His world is mostly a world of darkness, and only on rare occasions does the opossum go abroad by day. The darkness does two things: it serves as a cover for the opossum to move about, but it may also hide the movements of his enemies. The opossum is a different animal by night than he is in the daytime, according to most students. Typical is this description by Fitch and Sandidge, who studied the opossum on a preserve in Kansas.

On the few occasions when opossums were seen at night, their relative alertness and speed of movement contrasted with the sluggishness and seeming stupidity of those observed in daylight. Several were seen on roads in the beam of automobile headlights. These were quick to escape, running into thick roadside vegetation to elude pursuit. Others were found in woodland, with the aid of a powerful flashlight as the investigator moved about on foot. They did not permit close approach, and escaped by running. One hid in a blackberry thicket. Several that were chased climbed trees when hard pressed. One that was overtaken, and others that were shaken out of trees and caught, showed fight, standing on the defensive, and slashing at the pursuer with a rapidity and vigor never encountered in those removed from traps in the daytime.

Fitch and Sandidge also found a variety of reactions in opossums taken in traps that were run in daylight hours. Usually the animals were curled up in a deep sleep from which they did not arouse until they were touched or the trap was shaken. A far contrast from the behavior described above! "Reactions to humans varied greatly in individuals and was not necessarily correlated with age or sex," they reported. Adult males invariably were hostile and growled, with backs arched and hair bristling. Many adult females and the young of both sexes also exhibited this hostile behavior, but others did not. Some cowered silently, and others showed no uneasiness at all. A small proportion feigned death when handled or even before they were touched. But in daylight hours, even the opossums that made hostile gestures would hold their posture for less than a minute if the trapper made no further movements. They would then slowly turn their heads and start walking away "with deliberate gliding movements," often pausing abruptly in midstride. After moving away a few yards they would accelerate their pace in a scramble for shelter, but an occasional individual would move away unhurriedly, even foraging as it went. This last behavior is reminiscent of Wiedorn's description of opossums recovering slowly from the death feint.

Thus the opossum's seeming slowness by day gives way to an aggressive alertness in the hours of darkness, and it would seem this animal is not nearly as helpless or vulnerable as we might imagine. It goes its inquisitive way, probing here, poking there, seeking the insects and small rodent prey it loves, and investigating every nook and cranny. But all the while its senses, keenly tuned to darkness, are warning of possible danger. Thus it roves the autumn nights, feeding well in the fullness of summer's production, unaware of and uncaring for what winter may hold.

Winter

WINTER FOR THE OPOSSUM can be many things. Since its range stretches from subtropical Florida into Ontario, Canada, there are opossums that never know winter and many thousands of others that succumb to crushing cold.

Over much of the opossum's range, winter is a lean time. In all but the northernmost parts, winter is only occasionally severe. Snow does not persist nor is it often very deep. But it is a time of bare landscapes and scanty food. The opossum's weight reflects this shortage of food, declining considerably from late summer and fall's fat-gathering days.

Winter on the eastern plains area and northward, into the Great Lakes and New England country, can be a terrible ordeal for the opossum. On the open prairies, cover to escape winter's blasts is sparse, and the range is reduced to wooded stream courses, and the most dense ones, at that. The Great Lakes and New England regions are places of deep snows that often persist for long periods of time. Travel abroad for the short-legged opossum is greatly hampered and at times well-nigh impossible. During the winter the northern opossums face a much grimmer ordeal than their more southern cousins. Every investigator has found their numbers markedly reduced following a severe winter, as many thousands perish from cold and starvation.

In earlier decades, before opossums had spread their range so far to the north, winter was probably not such an ordeal. The deep South, with which the opossum is most often associated, does not have long periods of severe cold weather. Nevertheless, the occasional cold snaps must have taken their toll even there.

As mentioned earlier, opossums are frequently found with ears and

Opossums dislike being abroad in snow or daylight, but winter hunger sometimes forces them out.

tails frozen. These are the survivors; many others must have died from either the stress of the cold or the gangrene that may follow such severe skin-tissue damage. The large, thin ears seem especially susceptible to frostbite, and almost all older animals found in the northern parts of the range exhibit at least some damage to the ears. The tips of opossum tails also often show damage from freezing, though not as commonly as do the ears.

Because female opossums are more likely to hole up and wait out

94

An opossum does not seem at home in deep snow.

95

Most northern opossums emerge from winter with frozen ears.

periods of extremely cold weather, they exhibit less damage to ears and tail than do the males. But opossums are not hibernators; that is, they are not animals that undergo a deep, trancelike sleep during winter as jumping mice and woodchucks do, so they must eventually move out to find food to keep their bodily processes going.

Opossums of either sex display a tendency to lie low when the temperature dips below 20 degrees. As long as they can, they will attempt to wait out a winter cold spell or storm in their snug retreats. But hunger soon forces them to forage for food over a winter landscape. The males seemingly need more food at this time of year than the females, or possibly something in the nervous nature of the males forces them to activity when the female is more patient. At any rate, the males are abroad before the females venture out. It is especially during winter weather that human beings occasionally see opossums out in daylight hours, possibly because night-time hunting fails to produce enough food to meet the increased demands winter makes on us all.

Winter may force the opossum to shift its territory to areas of better food supplies, more cover for moving around, and better denning situ-

Taking time out to wash tail. Note loss of frozen tip.

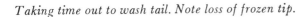

Trail of opossum in snow.

ations. Its feeding on fruit, for example, is partly from preference and partly from availability. As the fruit and plant supply fades through late autumn and early winter, the opossum reverts to its search for insects and animal foods. Hackberry, crabapple, and corn continued in the opossum's winter diet in Kansas, according to one report, but an Illinois study by Stieglitz and Klimstra revealed that the percentage of animal food in the opossum's diet increased from 52.2 per cent in late summer to 93.4 per cent in winter, while the importance of plant foods in the diet diminished during the period in almost exact proportion.

According to this study, the appearance of mammalian food in the opossum's diet increased by over 300 per cent between late summer and winter. As other foods diminish with winter, the opossum turns more and more to mammal carrion to sustain itself. This was inferred from the marked increase in utilization of carcasses of such large mammals as gray fox, striped skunk, raccoon, woodchuck, and even opossum. Certainly the opossum is not large enough to tackle such creatures if they were alive and healthy, so they must have been carrion.

Cottontail rabbit appeared rarely in the opossum's diet in the warm months, increasing during autumn and early winter. These animals might be those shot and lost by hunters. Cottontail in the diet declined in late winter, probably in concert with the decline of the cottontail population, but also the decline in hunting activity. Other small mam-

In winter, opossums may feed off the carcasses of striped skunk.

A fallen tree makes an easy travel lane.

mals tend to become more vulnerable in winter, as hiding coverts become thinner or much reduced. Thus such creatures as prairie voles were found with increasing frequency in the opossums studied as winter wore on.

Birds, too, turned up in Illinois opossum scats and stomachs, probably victims of winter weather, though they were almost absent in opossum diet in autumn and only minor in the warmer months. Their use was 29.8 per cent by volume in winter. Over four fifths of this total was domestic chicken and grackle, it was reported.

100

Winter

The opossum seldom follows a beaten path, even one of his own making, but is continually making little loops and side forays in its search for food. This activity is accelerated in winter, when it must search more actively for its various foods. But unless driven too hard by hunger, the opossum never goes too far from a stream or other water, where it feeds on crustaceans, especially crayfishes, during the cooler months of the year.

Dens are important to the opossum as places to spend the daytime hidden from prying eyes. They are doubly important in winter, when

An opossum likes nothing better than a den tree escape hole.

Opossum den in a fissure of a limestone bluff.

they also provide snug shelter from the cold. To the opossum a den means mostly a hole, though such holes may be in a variety of sites.

In Mississippi opossums use cavities in horizontal logs, holes in the ground, and cavities in standing trees; they also den in piles of debris, tree stumps, vine tangles, squirrel nests, and the attics of abandoned houses. Ground burrows of various kinds, usually woodchuck holes, are

102

frequent denning sites for opossums. These inquisitive, searching creatures investigate all such burrows as a matter of course on a winter
night's prowl, and occasionally they occupy them for a time.

Of 45 dens located in central Missouri, 23 were cavities in rocky
slopes. Much of Missouri has limestone ledges and outcroppings that are
broken by fractures and faults. These result in the formation of numerous
small caverns that afford excellent protection against both adverse
weather and enemies, and when they are available they seem to be

Woodchuck digs burrows used by opossums for dens.

preferred by opossums over any other type of shelter. Four dens were in old ground burrows that had been dug by woodchucks, five were in large trash heaps, four in old squirrel nests, three in hollow trees, three under farm buildings, two in horizontal logs on the ground, and one under a beehive.

Mrs. Lola Voss of Brownington, Missouri, once wrote me:

I was thinking how modern farm machinery has affected, in many different ways, the life of many small animals. In the days of the thresher there were many old strawstacks left in the fields and an old wheat stack was very durable, and there were many unused stacks of hay or spoiled hay. These made grand winter homes for opossums.

I remember one very cold winter day when the ground was covered with snow and my son was about 13 or 14. With a tiny, tan terrier and a neighborhood boy, he hunted all day, going from one old strawstack to another, all over the countryside. They sent the terrier—a willing accomplice—down all the holes in the stack and often she came backing out with an opossum about as large as she was. Finally she became tired and footsore and decided she'd "had it." She'd go down into the holes and just stay, so they had to call it a day. They had all the opossums they wanted to pack home as it was.

One female opossum carrying young was found in an abandoned squirrel nest which had been greatly enlarged by the addition of dry grass, corn husks, and oak leaves. This was on prairie land, and farmers in the vicinity reported that use of such nests by opossums was not uncommon, under the circumstances. In other prairie lands, in Illinois, opossums were found using squirrel denning boxes that had been erected, which they had made comfortable with corn husks and leaves. Good pragmatists, making the best of the situation if ground burrows or rock dens aren't available, the opossums will utilize any other shelter that affords warmth and security.

There is usually a slight preponderance of males over females in the general population at any season of the year, and more young than

Gray squirrel builds leafy nests used by opossums.

adults. This indicates that opossums in the wild are not especially long-lived. Probably two years would be the average life span. This is not surprising, as most wild creatures live fairly short lives, and the opossum, victim of many predators, is subject to a number of diseases and parasites that may either kill it or weaken its resistance to the point where it is easy prey for other creatures.

Raymond Hock, writing of the opossum in its fairly new home of Arizona, believes the opossum is one of the most heavily parasitized of all American mammals. He reports that they carry tularemia and endemic typhus fever in some localities. Kansas opossums studied were heavily infested with ticks and chiggers, so much so that animals in

105

summer were often found to be emaciated and shaggy-furred. Opossums commonly are host to mites, fleas, roundworms, flukes, and tapeworms as well, as might be expected from their habits and food-getting methods.

A total of eight species of trematodes were taken from opossums caught in the Reelfoot Lake area of Tennessee. During the summer of 1940 three scientists removed twenty specimens of a fluke, *Paragonimus westermani,* from the lungs of a single opossum taken in a trap there. This fluke had not previously been reported from opossums.

In Oklahoma two opossums were found to harbor, respectively, seven and twenty-six specimens of a new spiruroid stomach nematode, *Spirocerca longispiculata.* Near Athens, Georgia, an opossum was found to be parasitized by an undescribed coccidian of the genus *Isospora.*

Because they are not as fast as some other animals and possibly because they are so vulnerable when "playing possum," these animals suffer many broken bones, cuts, scratches, and other injuries. Broken ribs are common, as are broken shoulder blades. These might come from being seized and shaken by dogs or other predators.

The docile nature of opossums apparently prevents their being too severely hurt or crippled by traps. A study of steel trapping of small mammals made on the Wheeler National Wildlife Refuge revealed that of 962 opossums trapped only 19 were crippled, because they did not thrash around or gnaw on their trapped feet. This is a good thing for the opossums, since one seldom recovers from the loss of a foot. Other students found that opossums marked by toe clipping suffered wounds that healed only with great difficulty and after a considerable time.

Another threat to the opossum's existence may come from man's use of toxic insecticides of the chlorinated hydrocarbon type or other broad-spectrum killers. Aerial spraying of farmland near Sheldon, Illinois, at the rate of three pounds of dieldrin per acre, was fatal to some opossums, among other creatures. The area was not considered particularly attractive to opossums, but three were found dead within the treated area when the cropland was searched intensively following spraying, and another dead opossum was found the next year when searching was less intensive. Two of the four dead opossums were found at the edge of a stream.

So little is known positively about the effects of insecticides on all wildlife that we can only guess at the possible effects on the opossum. Any creature that makes so great a part of its diet from insects, as does the opossum, must surely be adversely affected by the widespread use of insecticides, if not directly, then at least indirectly.

The many things going against the opossum have been a cause for marvel for a long time. The French amateur naturalist Le Page du Pratz observed in 1718, "I have always been surprised at the great numbers of this small animal everywhere, when everything seems to conspire to their destruction." John Lawson, who was puzzled by the same thing, observed, "If a cat has nine lives, this creature has nineteen."

The Opossum and Man

SINCE THE FIRST SPANIARDS met the opossum it has figured in human tales, anecdotes, and folklore. But long before the white man met this inoffensive little beast, the American Indians had taken it into their own art, legends, and folkways. Indians of Mexico and Yucatan depicted the opossum in highly stylized ways, but almost always readily identifiable, no matter how bizarre the form.

In the area that was to become the United States, the opossum was also chosen as an art figure and possibly had some ceremonial or totemic significance. The Hopewell Culture, which many think dates roughly between 500 B.C. and A.D. 500, was noted for lovely little pipes of stone, carved in the shapes of various animals. One such pipe was an opossum figure, easily identified by the usual opossum characteristics of sharp snout, the way the eyes were indicated, and the scaly tail.

Much later in time (A.D. 800—1400), but before the white man had begun to take over the continent, people of the Middle Mississippian Culture were making wonderful pottery bowls, jugs, and bottles in both human and animal form. It is conjectured that such ceramics were ceremonial in purpose, for they are almost always found to be associated with burials. Sure enough, here, too, the opossum turns up as a subject for faithful reproduction. One such ceramic, in the collection of Edward Buel of Jefferson City, is illustrated here.

Such an unusual animal was bound to be noticed by the native American, whose life depended upon his observation and knowledge of the life around him. The opossum, where he was found, was well known. The ancient Cherokees regarded the opossum along with most other nocturnal and predatory animals, as "unclean." Their meat was

Hooded water bottle with opossum effigy from an Indian burial mound in Mississippi County, Arkansas, excavated in the 1920's, now in the Edward Buel collection. Photo by Thomas Buel.

not eaten because it was believed that these creatures were subject to blood revenge of their victims, but southeastern United States tribes are said to have used the hair of opossums for weaving and made girdles and garters from spun opossum hair.

The Seminoles used the opossum as the subject of a story and song, as recorded by Frances Densmore. It was part of a sad little tale that appeared in Densmore's report as follows.*

* From *Seminole Music,* published by the Smithsonian Institution, Bureau of American Ethnology, Bulletin No. 161, 1956.

The Opossum and Her Lost Baby

When Panther [the author's informant] was a boy, four to six years of age, his father told him this story which is presented in practically his own words. John Billie, an old man, said that he also heard the song when he was a child.

"An old opossum had a little baby. She was going somewhere and carried the baby along, all the time.

"The opossum found some wild potatoes and put the baby down while she dug the potatoes. She went away a little distance and every little while she called the baby, and it answered. [The narrator imitated the call and answer.] When the opossum came back she found that someone had stolen the baby and taken it away. The answer had come from a frog, put where the baby had been.

"Then the opossum looked around and found somebody's tracks. She followed the tracks. She was lonesome and she sang a song. She sang it four times, once with each of the stops that she made on her way to find the baby. There is only one word in the song, and that is I-ya-ta-wa-kits-ko-tic, which was the baby's name."

No. 229   *The Opossum Calls Her Lost Baby*   (Catalog No. 2139)
Recorded by Panther

"She came to a house. Somebody was there and she asked if they had seen anybody going by, carrying a baby. The person in the house said, 'Yes.' The opossum went in the direction they indicated and on the road she met two people and asked them the same question. Then she had been to two places and met two people, and sang her 'lonesome song' twice.

"After a while she came to another place. In that place the baby had been hidden. There were four or five houses, some occupied and some empty. The opossum asked her question and somebody pointed to a house saying, 'They got the baby in there.' She went over, opened the

110

door, and found the baby inside. Somebody had killed a rattlesnake, cooked it, and given it to the baby to eat. The mother was angry and told them to take it away. She took the baby and started home. She killed a little fawn, ate some of the meat, and gave some to the baby. They stayed there a while. That made three times she sang the song.

"A wolf came to that place and smelled the meat. The opossum lied and said she had no meat, but the wolf smelled the meat. The wolf got a bow and arrow. Then the opossum was afraid she would be killed. She went up a big tree, took the baby with her, and stayed up in the top of the tree. The baby died up there in the tree. That was the fourth time she sang the song.

"The old opossum came down and walked away. She found a skunk who was her friend and went home with the skunk. They lay down together and sang. They sang another 'lonesome song' and then they both died. This is the last song."

No. 230   *The Opossum Dies*   (CATALOG No. 2140)

♩ = 160   (1)   Recorded by Panther
                  (1)

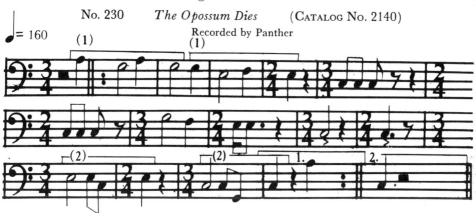

It would seem from this sad tale that the Seminoles have a fellow feeling for the poor opossum and believe it lives a tragic life. Those familiar with this tribe's history can sympathize with such an attitude.

Of course the white man, who gradually usurped the Indian's continent, was considerably interested in the opossum; there was nothing in the European fauna that resembled it. Its odd, nocturnal habits, the Indian tales about the animal, and especially its pouch excited a lot of interest. Some of the earliest descriptions and writings on this strange beast make interesting reading.

Richard Eden, writing in 1555, had this to say:

Emonge these trees is fownde that monstrous beaste with a snowte lyke a foxe, a tayle lyke a marmasette, eares lyke a batte, handes lyke a man, and feete lyke an ape, bearing her whelpes abowte with her in an owtwarde bellye much lyke unto a greate bagge or purse.

Eden went on to recount the suckling and care of the young until they were able to fend for themselves and bemoaned the fact that the captured opossum specimen perished, sometime after her young died, possibly because of dietary deficiencies in captivity. Eden's work was based on an earlier account by Peter Martyr.

Naturally the unusual tail of the opossum came in for its place in folklore. According to early Spanish writers, the tail was used medicinally and for many ailments among the Indians. Wrote one Spanish friar:

It [the tail] has great medicinal value: it draws out, through many applications, any ailment of the flesh or bone; and women who are in labor, if they drink a little of the steeped tail of this animal, give birth immediately; those who are constipated are cured at once by drinking a little of the extract because it opens and cleanses the pores; those who have a cough get well by drinking this broth.

Other writers copied such writings and even improved on them, adding to the curative powers of the opossum's tail.

The Spanish were the first in the field so far as the opossum is concerned; the English produced no firsthand descriptive writing about the beast until nearly a century after the Spanish. One of the most quoted descriptions of the opossum is Captain John Smith's:

An Opassom hath an head like a Swine, and a taile like a Rat, and is of the bignes of a Cat. Under her belly she hath a bagge, wherein shee lodgeth, carrieth, and sucketh her young.

Modern writers almost never neglect to use this quote of Captain Smith's, which was not the first description by an Englishman (that honor

112

belongs to naturalist Thomas Harriot) but has certainly become the most popular. Incidentally, the name "Virginia opossum" came down to us as the proper name from these English colonists, who settled first in what was in reality the northern part of the opossum's range at that time.

Rene Robert Cavelier, Sieur de la Salle, is credited with being the first Frenchman to meet the opossum. He is reported by the chronicler, Father Hennepin, to have come into camp after a night's absence with two of the creatures hanging from his belt. He had killed them with a stick. These two luckless creatures are featured in a famous painting, "La Salle at the Portage," by Arthur Thomas, now in the courthouse of St. Joseph County, Indiana. They are shown dangling from the explorer's belt as he greets Father Hennepin.

La Salle's swatting the two opossums with a stick (Father Hennepin notes they made no attempt to fight or flee) is only one of many collisions of man and opossum. The opossum invariably comes off second best. Neither the red man nor the white seems to have had any special affinity for the opossum. Mrs. Lola Voss, quoted earlier, once wrote me what seems to sum up most men's opinions of the opossum.

To paraphrase our Miss Dove, the opossum is *not* a lovely beast. Miss Dove would elucidate further on the beneficent qualities of her beast, but doggone if I can think of a thing to say about the opossum.

The result of such an attitude is for man to generally consider the opossum a nuisance at best. He is seldom mourned when slain by a speeding auto—and quite a good many opossums perish this way. Rather than say anything good about the creature, most rural folk consider the opossum a potential chicken thief. Unfortunately, there is evidence to back them up. Opossums do occasionally raid chicken houses.

Again quoting Mrs. Voss:

When roused out of deep slumber and a warm bed in the middle of the night, by the frightened squalling of terrified hens, and donning my fighting gear, to stalk out and find one of the creatures grinning up at me from the half-eaten carcass of one of the hens, I always feel we could do with one less opossum and invariably this comes to pass.

Lest the reader think that statement comes from someone predisposed to hate the opossum, let me quote the rest of the passage, which is probably the attitude of most thoughtful persons with respect to our wild creatures.

It is nice to know that its habitat is so far-reaching. I should hate to think we are scraping the bottom of the barrel opossum-wise. The extinction of any of our little fellow creatures seems to me a sad commentary on the stupidity of the human race. A part of our heritage, lost forever, is saddening, whether of plant or animal or pure air and water.

The opossum has a built-in life insurance in his habit of sulling that probably often pays dividends. I can recall my mother coming in from the chicken house one dark night and complacently remarking on the feat of killing an opossum that was after the hens. She laid the victim out on the steps near the chicken house. We could see it in the morning, she said. Some time in the night the corpse got up and walked away.

Besides collisions of man and opossum in the chicken house, they sometimes meet in other ways. Opossums will take up residence in the foundations of houses, and I have heard of them setting up housekeeping in the walls, occasionally being inconsiderate enough to die there. This strains relations, too.

There was a time when opossums were trapped by man for both food and fur. Farm boys used to make most of their spending money by running trap lines, and the opossum was a never-failing source of cash. Their nosiness made them fairly easy to trap and, unlike more savage animals, they seldom escaped. Trapping opossums was most common in the South, which was opossum heartland. Old-timers can remember when a number-one opossum pelt brought two dollars, and even commons would bring a dollar. That was worthwhile money to young and old alike, back in Depression days, when both food and money were scarce.

All that is changed today. During the 1940's excise taxes were slapped on fur garments, which had a depressing effect on the use of certain furs. As long as a person was going to pay a fancy price, plus a heavy excise tax on a fur coat, he might as well get the best, and opossum fur ranked well down the list, so far as desirable furs were concerned. Then fashion took a hand; milady wanted the short furs, rather than the long furs. Fox, raccoon, and opossum fur declined, and the short furs such as mink and muskrat gained in popularity.

For a short time there was even a trend away from fur garments entirely, as new miracle fibers were introduced that offered some of the same virtues as fur. Today the fur industry is holding its own, but opossum pelts are still not in great demand.

The fur industry may be one of the world's oldest businesses, since furs were mankind's first clothes. As far back as 2,000 B.C. furs had considerable value and were mentioned as booty of war. Furs were introduced into Europe as fashion items by the Crusaders and became the clothing symbols of the nobility and clergy. It was the quest for furs that was responsible for the exploration and opening of the United States and Canada.

The fur industry today is highly speculative, and the value of furs is constantly shifting according to several factors. One is economics: the fur industry is one of the first hit in a period of deflation, since its products are considered luxury items. Supply and demand play a part in evaluating certain furs and rarity controls the price. Most fickle of all controlling factors is fashion. Any change in the whims of fashion designers can make or break the market in certain types of fur. For example, long-haired furs were in disfavor as garment items for several years and trapping and selling of them extremely slow. But when the Davy Crockett craze hit American youth and a demand for coonskin caps caused a rush on the warehouses for long-haired furs, all sorts—

from rabbit to raccoon to opossum—went into "coonskin" caps.

Durability is also a factor in a fur's popularity and use; certain furs were better than others. Ratings are based on the sea otter's pelt, which is one of the most durable of all. The following table ranking the most common furs, including the opossum, shows why opossum fur is one of the less desirable furs in this respect.

Fur Animal	Durability
Otter	100
Beaver	90
Mink	70
Raccoon	65
Muskrat	45
Fox	40
Opossum (natural)	37
Opossum (dyed)	20
Squirrel	25
Rabbit	5

The U.S. Bureau of Sports Fisheries and Wildlife reports that in 1963–1964 a total of 167,353 opossums was harvested throughout the nation. Oddly enough, the top opossum state that trapping season was not in the South but in Indiana, which reported 41,000 opossums pelted. Missouri was second, with 29,000, and Ohio third with almost 12,000 opossums harvested.

Back in 1946–1947 fur trapping was much more extensive and intensive than it is today and, instead of 29,000 opossums, Missouri reported an annual take of 336,643, more than double the entire 1963–1964 harvest. They were worth an average of seventy-five cents apiece, then, and meant a cash return to trappers of $252,480.25. Opossum led all other species in numbers taken, but of course not in cash value. From 1940 to 1950 the average annual take of opossums in Missouri was 288,000, but this dwindled to 26,488 in 1957–1958, when the average

Up a tree: it's no trick at all for a good climber.

price per pelt was only fifteen cents and the annual value of the harvest only $3,973.20.

During the 1963–1964 trapping season the value of opossum pelts ranged, nationwide, from a high of fifty cents to a low of twenty-two cents, with an average value of only thirty-four cents. Certainly this low value is a reflection in the changes that have taken place in the fur

117

Possum hunting.

industry with respect to species like the opossum. Without the economic incentive—and most boys today would not consider thirty-four cents worth the effort of rising early on winter mornings to run a trap line and skinning and pelting the catch—trapping in most of the United States is a gradually passing thing. There are other incentives, such as the sporting aspect of trapping, but these seem to be overborne by the economic considerations.

The Bureau of Sports Fisheries and Wildlife figures for 1963–1964 show that the actual number of opossums harvested that year had declined 39 per cent from the previous year and prices paid were down

Possum hunting.

an average of 13 per cent.

Although opossum trapping appears to be declining, opossum hunting has and probably will continue to be an important sport, especially in the South. Thousands enjoy the opossum as prey to hunt and know the toothsome eating he provides, though the opossum's hide is hardly worth the skinning. To such sportsmen as these, opossums are important game animals.

Most opossum hunting is done at night, when they are abroad seeking food. The technique is much like raccoon hunting; a dog is trained to trail and tree. One difference is that raccoon hunters like chilly, wet weather, while one can have a good opossum hunt on nights when raccoon hunters are more inclined to stay at home.

An opossum dog can be just about any breed. Semi-retired raccoon dogs are used, although prime raccoon dogs are discouraged from trailing the opossum. Any breed you can train to trail and tree will do the job, and often mutts and run-of-the-mill curs make the best opossum dogs.

Training is easy. The usual technique is to walk a live opossum along,

Possum hunting.

holding on to its tail, until you lay a scent track to a small tree. Leave the opossum up the tree and take the young dog to the trail's start. He'll usually follow it and can be urged to start barking when he discovers the opossum. A few such lessons and you've got a hunter.

Opossums, once treed, can be shot out or captured alive. Real opossum eaters like to take them alive. They are kept in captivity for a couple of weeks and well fed, to fatten them up. Then comes the eating.

Three of my favorite recipes come from *Cy Littlebee's Guide to Cooking Fish and Game,* compiled by W. O. Nagel, of the Missouri Department of Conservation. Try these:

Judge Thomas V. Proctor's Recipe—Roast Opossum Supreme

Opossum is extremely fat and has a very peculiar flavor. However, if prepared correctly and cooked with care it can be one of the most delicious entrees that can be found in our local game.

To dress, immerse in very hot water (not boiling, however) for one minute. Next remove hair (like scraping a hog) with a dull knife or a hog scraper, so that the skin is not cut. Next slit from neck to hind legs, and remove entrails. Wash thoroughly inside and out with hot water, remove head and tail if desired. Cover with cold water to which has been added one cup of salt and let stand overnight: in morning drain off salt water and rinse again with boiling water.

Make a stuffing as follows: brown one large, finely chopped onion in one tablespoon of butter, add chopped opossum liver and heart and cook until tender, add two cups of browned bread crumbs, a chopped bay leaf and a small chopped red pepper, a finely chopped hard-boiled egg, a generous dash of Worcestershire sauce, salt and pepper to taste, moisten with three or four tablespoons of water. Stuff opossum with above mixture and sew up opening with large needle and coarse thread. Roast in oven roaster on wire rack at 350 degrees until it is tender and richly brown. Serve on heated platter, skim fat from gravy and serve with baked yams, grits, watercress salad, wild plum jelly and spoon bread. If the above directions are followed you will have a treat that you will never forget.

Art Pugh, conservation agent at Higginsville, Missouri, says the following is an old southern recipe:

Possum and Sweet Taters

This is a recipe my father, J. Conley Pugh, of Grandview, picked up many years ago from other Southern families living along the Little Blue.

After you skin and clean your possum, trim all fat off the carcass. Freeze if possible.

When you are ready to cook the varmint place it in a roaster. Place an onion and an apple inside the possum, then sprinkle with salt, pepper, and sage. (Other spices may be used to suit taste.) Put enough water in roaster to keep meat from scorching. Cover, place in oven at low heat and steam one hour (varying slightly with size of animal). Uncover, place sweet potatoes around possum, replace cover and cook until potatoes are tender. Uncover and brown the possum.

Lastly, this recipe from Mrs. A. A. Heinze, of Imperial, Missouri, writer and broadcaster:

Opossum and Sweet Potatoes

The following directions were given to me by an elderly woman who was more of Indian blood than French.

In preparing the opossum my instructor preferred to leave the skin on the opossum, scraping and singeing the hair off and scrubbing the skin with soap and water and rinsing thoroughly with clear water afterward. The opossum, drawn and cleaned, was then parboiled until slightly tender; the water was then drained off and the opossum placed in a baking pan into which was melted a cupful of bacon grease.

Sweet potatoes, as many as desired to pile around the opossum, were scrubbed with the skins on, and boiled until slightly soft before putting in the pan with the opossum. I should judge that the moderately heated oven meant about 350 degrees in our modern electric or gas stoves. The baking time was never really timed for wild game cooked by my French-Indian instructor, but she basted the meat until she knew it was done by the golden brown color and when it could be pierced with a fork.

That's enough for recipes. It gets my mouth watering, just writing them down from the cookbook.

The Opossum and Man

Before I leave the subject of eating opossums, however, let me tell about a gourmet's club in Newnan, Georgia, that was reported in the *Georgia Game and Fish* magazine.

Most people tend to deprecate the opossum, and there is a tendency to look down both on it and those who hunt or eat it. Often such opossum buffs are considered "low class." Newnan, in Coweta County, Georgia, gives the lie to any such notion. Each year since 1912, the Coweta County 'Possum Eaters has held a convention, the main course being, naturally, 'possum and sweet 'taters. Lowbrow? Not on your life! Coweta County, southwest of Atlanta, is said to be the wealthiest per-capita area in Georgia, and the Coweta County 'Possum Eaters' place cards read like the Newnan Bluebook.

To quote from *Game and Fish* magazine:

This unique convention of 'possum-on-the-platter fanciers developed from a quiet, informal get-together of two Newnan citizens back in 1912 to a present organization numbering almost 200 members. This growth has taken place despite the fact that membership in the Club is hard to come by. Before it was moved into larger facilities, new members were admitted only when a member died or moved away. . . . The best way to get a place at the 'possum table is to inherit it. Power, position or influence won't help.

This exclusive club originated when two prominent Newnan citizens, J. A. Blakely and Henry Richards, returned from a successful opossum hunt and brought their animals to Bud Gay, a restaurateur, for his special preparation. They invited three ministers to be their guests and both hosts and guests alike agreed to hold another banquet the following year. According to *Game and Fish:*

It was not long until 'possum eating enthusiasts crowded Bud's small restaurant to capacity and the Club was forced to close its doors to hungry latecomers. Bud Gay became famous for his 'possum, 'taters, and Bud Gay gravy. He continued to serve platters of 'possum with all his special trimmings to these happy few until his death in 1946.

123

The World of the Opossum

Most of the old-timers are gone, but the tradition of these founding 'Possum Eaters lives on. At the recent Convention, 162 pounds of mouth-watering roast 'possum and two bushel baskets of baked sweet potatoes were quickly consumed by eager Eaters—a veritable Georgia eating orgy!

An opossum hunt and the singular behavior of the opossum in "playing possum" got into our literature many years ago in a verse written by some unknown savant, who drew on his schoolboy Latin to tell his tale. My mother, who later became a Latin teacher herself, recalls that the high school set of her day enjoyed this verse, a pleasant relief from Caesar's *Gallic Wars*.

Carmen Possum*

The nox was lit by lux of luna,
And 'twas a nox most opportuna
To catch a possum or a coona;
For nix was scattered o'er this mundus,
A shallow nix, et non profundus.
On sic a nox with canis unus,
Two boys went out to hunt for coonus.
The corpus of this bonus canis
Was full as long as octo span is,
But brevior legs had canis never
Quam had hic dog; et bonus clever,
Some used to say, in stultum jocum
Quod a field was too small locum
For sic a dog to make a turnus
Circum self from stem to sternus.
Unis canis, duo puer,
Nunquam braver, nunquam truer,
Quam hoc trio nunquam fuit,
If there was I never knew it.
This bonus dog had one bad habit,
Amabat much to tree a rabbit,

---

* From *The Best Loved Poems of the American People,* selected by Hazel Felleman, Garden City Publishing Co., Garden City, N.Y., 1936.

The Opossum and Man

Amabat plus to chase a rattus,
Amabat bene tree a cattus.
But on this nixy moonlight night
This old canis did just right.
Nunquam treed a starving rattus,
Nunquam chased a starving cattus.
But sucurrit on, intentus
On the track and on the scentus,
Till he trees a possum strongum,
In a hollow trunkum longum.
Loud he barked in horrid bellum,
Seemed on terra vehit pellum.
Quickly ran the duo puer
Mors of possum to secure.
Quam venerit, one began
To chop away like quisque man.
Soon the axe went through the truncum
Soon he hit it all kerchunkum;
Combat deepens, on ye braves!
Canis, pueri et staves;
As his powers non longius tarry,
Possum potest, non pugnare.
On the nix his corpus lieth.
Down to Hades spirit flieth,
Joyful pueri, canis bonus,
Think him dead as any stonus.

Now they seek their pater's domo,
Feeling proud as any homo,
Knowing, certe, they will blossom
Into heroes, when with possum
They arrive, narrabunt story,
Plenus blood et plenior glory.
Pompey, David, Samson, Caesar,
Cyrus, Black Hawk, Shalmanezer!
Tell me where est now the gloria,
Where the honors of victoria?

Nunc a domum narrent story,
Plenus sanguine, tragic, gory.
Pater praiseth, likewise mater,
Wonders greatly younger frater.
Possum leave they on the mundus,
Go themselves to sleep profundus,
Somniunt possums slain in battle,
Strong as ursae, large as cattle.
When nox gives way to lux of morning,
Albam terram much adorning,
Up they jump to see the varmen,
Of the which this is the carmen.
Lo! possum est resurrectum!
Ecce pueri dejectum,
Ne relinquit track behind him,
Et the pueri never find him.
Cruel possum! bestia vilest,
How the pueros thou beguilest!
Pueri think non plus of Caesar,
Go ad Orcum, Shalmanezer,
Take your laurels, cum the honor,
Since ista possum is a goner!

"Carmen Possum" may not be great poetry, but it was enjoyed by budding classicists of long ago and was remembered fondly enough to get into a great anthology.

A good many rural youngsters have brought opossums home, either the survivors of their trap lines or sometimes the offspring of a mother opossum that has met an accidental death. They have been nurtured and kept alive, but opossums do not make good pets. It should be obvious that the pets man has kept through the millennia, particularly dogs and cats, *are* pets because they possess certain qualities that other animals do not; otherwise we would have a broader spectrum of pets than we have. Almost without exception, our common wild animals make poor pets, and the opossum is one of the most disappointing in

Don Wooldridge's daughter Ann and two of her opossum pets.

127

this respect.

Pets are attractive to man for a variety of reasons. They possess certain qualities that we like, such as intelligence, friendliness, interesting behavior, beauty, or some other quality. Alas! The poor opossum is wanting in almost all of these.

Hartman quotes from Brehm's *Tierleben:*

The opossum is plentiful and cheap on the animal market. But it is a dumb, dull pet, for its activity affords the owner little pleasure. I have seen none of that intelligence ascribed to it by Audubon. It is sluggish, lazy, sleepy, and forbiddingly stupid, at least in captivity.

Dr. Charles H. Townsend agrees:

A coyote on the prowl, a natural enemy of the opossum.

The Opossum and Man

Waiting for an opossum to do something interesting was evidently a matter of more time than I had to spare; so he was swung by the tail on to a shelf near the window, and just across the room from my desk, where if he ever did anything, I should be a witness. Nothing happened for an hour, when I placed a quarter of an apple under his nose and resumed my work.

After about 10 minutes, hearing a slight sound, I looked up to see the opossum holding the apple quarter in one hand, and rapidly but thoroughly chewing a mouthful. When the apple was finished he settled back somewhat on his haunches, and proceeded to wash his face cat-fashion, only he used both hands at once, licking his lips and fingers and then rubbing his nose and cheeks.

After that, nothing happened for half an hour, when I went over and stroked his back. This caused nervousness and a silly display of his teeth, but he crouched and submitted. No attempt was made to leave the shelf, and in the evening, the opossum was shut in an empty room just to make sure he wouldn't be abroad at night, after the fashion of opossums.

Opossums *are* most active at night, when you and I are least likely to enjoy them as pets. My own adult opossums would sleep all day, though they would crawl about their cages at night. If I awoke them during the day they exhibited the usual sluggishness and, if handled very much, would make threatening displays. They never became what I would consider tame.

Young opossums easily learn to tolerate human handling, and they have the winsomeness of all young animals. Once they outgrow their appealing youthful stages, however, they offer little to interest human beings. Opossums do not seem to display much discernment as to their benefactors and lack the affectionate displays that endear dogs and cats to us.

What about the future of the opossum? Its mythology and place in man's folklore seem assured, but is the opossum likely to continue to exist? I think so. As I mentioned earlier, any animal that has endured through the millenia, virtually unchanged, with some of the world's

129

greatest beasts passing into oblivion as it went quietly on its way, is not likely to pass soon from this scene.

Wildlife biologists point to the rapid spread of the opossum into hitherto unoccupied range as an indication that man's use of the landscape thus far has not had a deleterious effect on its survival chances. I think this is generally true, but I wonder about those few opossums found dead in central Illinois following an experiment with dieldrin. Remember that at almost every season of the year the opossum depends heavily upon insects for food. This diet and its grubbing, nosing, scratching habits would seem to make it especially susceptible to chemical poisons. All the facts are not yet in with respect to insecticides. They may accomplish what all the fanged predators of creation have been unable to do.

What about the opossum's place in the biota? Is the opossum important to the plant and animal life around it, and especially to man? This may be an impertinent question, and I usually think it is, although well-meaning people frequently ask: What's it good for ? My answer to such a question is: It is good because it is there.

Religious consideration aside, what is *man* good for? The question put this way might give questioners pause, because we think our own being is justification enough. If the opossum were given to such speculation in its "low bean-power" brain, it would probably feel that its being was justification enough. Let's live and let live.

Man is a relatively recent arrival in the world and, although he has taken the quest for knowledge of his environment and its working further than any animal ever has, he still has a lot to learn. It is not given to us to know the importance of any single species to the entire fabric of life on this earth. Occasionally we get glimpses, though. Recall a few years ago when the federal government went on an extensive poisoning campaign against coyotes in the west. The population of rodents dramatically increased to the point that the arch foes of the coyote —the stockmen—were demanding its protection to help offset the rodent

Opossum peering from its den.

131

irruption. The coyote took a few sheep or calves, but only when it was reduced to near extinction in a part of its range could we see that it held an important place in the great tapestry of nature.

Earlier in this chapter I pointed out that most men either ignore the opossum or feel a certain vague hostility toward it, as a potential predator or pest. By and large they leave it alone, except as a sporting or trapping species. In neither case does man do any appreciable harm to the opossum as a species. Fur prices are so low that trapping for the opossum is insignificant, and hunting pressure in almost all the opossum's range is extremely light. If the opossum ultimately suffers any harm as a species from man, it will come in some inadvertent and probably unintended way, such as poisoning by insecticides. I like to believe most people feel, as Mrs. Voss wrote, that any loss of a wild creature is a saddening thing. Feeling this way, perhaps we will be less apt to blunder and cause its extinction.

Personally, I look forward to the opossum's being around a long time, because I *know* I'd miss the little creature. I no longer trap opossums and seldom hunt them, yet just occasionally running into them on a cold winter day's hike or seeing them scurry across the streets of town at night gives me a certain lift of spirit that I value very much. In a day when there is stress and worry about even man's future on the earth, we need the heartening sight of wild creatures, going their way of old, to give us a sense of stability.

Speaking of man's future on the earth, let me repeat the words of Chester Davis, writing about the opossum: "All told, it's a pretty good place, this world the possum expects to inherit. Contemplating man and his frantic ways, the philosophic opossum thinks, 'And this, too, shall pass away.' And don't you bet that it won't, either. That's the bet the dinosaur lost."

The opossum is still with us!

Opossum Subspecies

THE FOLLOWING LIST of subspecies of the opossum, *Didelphis marsupialis*, has been taken from *The Mammals of North America*, by E. Raymond Hall and Keith R. Kelson, Volume I, copyright © 1959 by The Ronald Press Company.

Didelphis marsupialis battyi Thomas. Known only from Coiba Island, Panama.

Didelphis marsupialis californica Bennett. Known principally from western and northwestern Mexico.

Didelphis marsupialis cozumelae Merriam. Known only from Cozumel Island, Yucatan.

Didelphis marsupialis etensis J. A. Allen. Type locality is Eten, Piura, Peru, but known also from Costa Rica.

Didelphis marsupialis insularis J. A. Allen. Known from Caparo, Trinidad, Island of Dominica, Martinque Island, St. Vincent Island, Grenada Island, and in the South American area on Trinidad Island.

Didelphis marsupialis pigra Bangs. Type locality from Oak Lodge, opposite Micco, Brevard County, Florida. Also known from South Carolina (Charleston), thence south and west along Atlantic Coast and Gulf of Mexico to Texas: Matagordo, Deming Station.

Didelphis marsupialis particeps Goldman. Known only from San Miguel Island, Golfo de Panama, Panama.

Didelphis marsupialis richmondi J. A. Allen. Known only from a

133

small area along the Nicaragua and Costa Rica border, specifically Greytown, Nicaragua, and San José, Costa Rica.

Didelphis marsupialis tabascensis J. A. Allen. Known from the states of Veracruz, Tabasco, and Chiapas in Mexico; Nicaragua.

Didelphis marsupialis texensis J. A. Allen. Known from south (Rockport) and west Texas (Monahans to the Pecos) and from adjoining northeastern Mexico.

Didelphis marsupialis virginiana Kerr. Presently occupying range from southern Ontario east to Massachusetts thence south to north of Charleston, S.C., westward through the states of Georgia, Alabama, Mississippi, Louisiana, and Texas through the panhandle to eastern Colorado, thence northeastward through central and eastern Nebraska, southern Minnesota and Wisconsin and the lower half of the Michigan peninsula. Also known from a small area of eastern Arizona (Alpine and Nogales) where it is introduced. Introduced and established in western Colorado near Grand Junction and along the entire western Pacific Coast, through California, Oregon, and Washington.

Didelphis marsupialis yucatanensis J. A. Allen. Known from northern Yucatan and British Honduras.

Bibliography

Allen, Durward L. "Nobody Loves the 'Possum," *Michigan Conservationist,* Vol. 9, No. 6, March, 1940.

————, and Warren Shapton. "An Ecological Study of Winter Dens, with Special Reference to the Eastern Skunk," *Ecology:* Vol. 23, No. 1, January, 1942.

Atkeson, Thomas Z. "Incidence of Crippling Loss in Steel Trapping," *Journal of Wildlife Management,* Vol. 20, No. 3, July, 1956.

Beidleman, Richard G. "Possums and Points West," *Colorado Conservationist;* Vol. 1, No. 4, July–August, 1952.

Bennitt, Rudolf, and W. O. Nagel. *A Survey of Resident Game and Furbearers of Missouri,* University of Missouri Studies, Vol. 12, No. 2, 1937.

Bradt, G. W. "Opossum—invader from the South," *Michigan Conservationist;* Vol. 16, No. 3, March–April, 1947.

Burns, Eugene. *The Sex Life of Wild Animals,* Rinehart and Company, Inc., New York, 1953.

Burt, William H. *The Mammals of Michigan,* The University of Michigan Press, Ann Arbor, 1948.

Burton, Maurice. *Systematic Dictionary of Mammals of the World,* Thomas Y. Crowell Company, New York, 1962.

Byrd, Elon E., and Robert J. Reiber. "Mammalian Trematodes. I. Trematodes from the Opossum, *Didelphis virginiana* Kerr," *Reelfoot Lakes Biological Station Reports,* Vol. 6, Reelfoot, Tennessee, 1942.

————, ————, and Malcolm V. Parker. "The Anatomy of a Lung Fluke from the Opossum (*Didelphis virginiana* Kerr)," *Reelfoot Lakes Biological Station Reports,* Vol. 6, Reelfoot, Tennessee, 1942.

Cockrum, E. Lendell. *Mammals of Kansas,* University of Kansas Publications, Museum of Natural History, Vol. 7, No. 1, August, 1952.

135

Coghill, G. E. "Studies on Rearing the Opossum," *Ohio Journal of Science,* Vol. 39, No. 5, September, 1939.

Davis, Chester. "The Peculiar Opossum," *Wildlife in North Carolina,* Vol. XXVII, No. 8, August, 1963.

"The Day the Opossum is King," *Georgia Game and Fish;* Vol. II, No. 2, Autumn, 1962.

Densmore, Frances. *Seminole Music,* Smithsonian Institution, Bureau of American Ethnology, Bulletin No. 161, 1956.

Denton, J. Fred. "The Occurrence of *Eurytrema allen-toshi* (Foster, 1939) in the Opossum in Texas," *Proceedings of the Helminthological Society,* Vol. 11, No. 2, Washington, D.C., 1944.

Dikmans, G. "The Occurrence of *Viannaia viannai travas-sos (Nematoda: Heligmosomidae)* in Opossums in North America," *Proceedings of the Helminthological Society,* Vol. 10, No. 1, Washington, D.C., 1943.

Doutt, J. Kenneth. "The Swimming of the Opossum, *Didelphis marsupialis virginiana,*" *Journal of Mammalogy,* Vol. 34, No. 4, November, 1954.

Ernst, Stanton G. "The Ramblin' Rebel," *The Maryland Conservationist,* Vol. XLI, No. 2, March–April, 1964.

Fitch, H. S., and Lewis L. Sandidge. *Ecology of the Opossum in a Natural Area in Northeastern Kansas.* University of Kansas Publications, Museum of Natural History, Vol. 7, 1953.

"Fur Catch of the United States, 1964," *Wildlife Leaflet* No. 471, Bureau of Sports Fisheries and Wildlife, U.S.D.I., Washington, D.C., September, 1965.

Gilbert, William H., Jr. *The Eastern Cherokees,* Smithsonian Institution, Bureau of American Ethnology, Bulletin No. 133, 1943.

Hall, E. Raymond and Keith R. Kelson. *The Mammals of North America,* Vol. I, The Ronald Press, New York, 1959.

Hamilton, William J., Jr. "Birth in the Opossum Family," *Pennsylvania Game News,* Vol. 13, No. 11, February, 1943.

———. "The Food of the Opossum in New York State," *Journal of Wildlife Management,* Vol. 15, No. 3, July, 1951.

——— *The Mammals of the Eastern United States,* Comstock Publishing Company, Inc., Ithaca, N.Y., 1943.

Bibliography

Hartman, Carl G. "Breeding Habits, Development and Birth of the Opossum," Smithsonian Institution, Report for 1921, 1922.

———. "The Breeding Season of the Opossum (*Didelphis virginiana*) and the Rate of Intra-uterine and Postnatal development," *Journal of Morphology and Physiology,* Vol. 46, 1928.

———. *Possums,* University of Texas Press, Austin, 1952.

Hesselschwert, R. E. "Use of Den Boxes in Wildlife Restoration on Intensively Farmed Areas," *Journal of Wildlife Management,* Vol. 6, 1942.

Hill, William C. *"Spirocerca longispiculata N. sp.,"* *American Midland Naturalist,* Vol. 21, No. 3, May, 1939.

Hock, Raymond J. "The Opossum in Arizona," *Journal of Mammalogy,* Vol. 33, No. 4, November, 1952.

Korschgen, Leroy J. "Food Habits of the Coyote in Missouri," *Journal of Wildlife Management,* Vol. 21, No. 4, October, 1957.

Lay, Daniel W. "Ecology of the Opossum in Eastern Texas," *Journal of Mammalogy,* Vol. 23, No. 2, May, 1942.

Llewellyn, L. M., and F. M. Uhler. "The Foods of Fur Animals of the Patuxent Research Refuge, Maryland," *American Midland Naturalist,* Vol. 48, No. 1, 1952.

——— and Fred H. Dale. "Notes on the Ecology of the Opossum in Maryland," *Journal of Mammalogy,* Vol. 45, No. 1, February, 1964, as cited in *Wildlife Review,* No. 113, March, 1964.

McCrady, E., Jr. "The Embryology of the Opossum," *American Anatomical Memoirs,* Vol. 16, 1938.

McKeever, Sturgis. "Reproduction in the Opossum in Southwestern Georgia and Northwestern Florida," *Journal of Wildlife Management,* Vol. 22, No. 3, July, 1958.

Milne, Lorus and Margery. *The Senses of Animals and Men,* Atheneum, New York, 1962.

Nagel, Werner O., ed. *Cy Littlebee's Guide to Cooking Fish and Game,* Missouri Conservation Commission, Jefferson City, Mo., 1959.

Palmer, Ralph S. *The Mammal Guide,* Doubleday & Company, New York, 1954.

Petrides, George A. "Sex and Age Determination in the Opossum," *Journal of Mammalogy,* Vol. 30, No. 4, November, 1949.

Reynolds, Harold C. "A Contribution of the Life History and Ecology of the Opossum, D.V., in Central Missouri," unpublished master's thesis, University of Missouri, 1942.

————. "Some Aspects of the Life History and Ecology of the Opossum in Missouri," *Journal of Mammalogy,* Vol. 26, No. 4, November, 1945.

————. *Studies of Reproduction in the Opossum* (D.v.v.), University of California Publications in Zoology, Vol. 52, No. 3, 1952.

————. "The Opossum," *Scientific American,* Vol. 188, No. 6, June, 1953.

Romer, Alfred S. *Vertebrate Paleontology,* 2nd ed., The University of Chicago Press, Chicago, 1946.

Sandidge, Lewis L. "Food and Dens of the Opossum (D.V.) in Northeastern Kansas," *Transactions of the Kansas Academy of Science,* Vol. 56, No. 1, 1953.

Schwartz, Charles W. and Elizabeth R. *The Wild Mammals of Missouri,* University of Missouri Press, Columbia, Mo., 1959.

————. "Opossum," *Missouri Conservationist,* Vol. 14, No. 7, 1953.

Scott, Thomas, Yuell L. Willis, and Jack A. Ellis. "Some Effects of a Field Application of Dieldrin on Wildlife," *Journal of Wildlife Management,* Vol. 23, No. 4, October, 1959.

Seton, Ernest Thompson. *Lives of Game Animals,* Charles T. Branford Company, Boston, 1953.

Smith, Luther. "An Observation on the Nest-building Behavior of the Opossum," *Journal of Wildlife Management,* Vol. XXII, No. 2, May, 1941.

Stieglitz, Walter O., and W. D. Klimstra. "Dietary Pattern of the Virginia Opossum, *Didelphis marsupialis virginianus* Kerr, Late Summer–Winter, Southern Illinois," *Transactions of the Illinois Academy of Science,* Vol. 55, Nos. 3 and 4, 1962.

Swanton, John R. *The Indians of the Southeastern United States,* Smithsonian Institution, Bureau of American Ethnology, Bulletin No. 137, 1946.

Taube, Clarence M. "Studies of the Occurrence, Growth, and Food Habits of the Opossum in Michigan," unpublished master's thesis, Michigan State College, 1942.

Bibliography

Taube, Clarence M. "Food Habits of the Michigan Opossum," *Journal of Wildlife Management,* Vol. 11, No. 1, January, 1947.

U.S. Fish and Wildlife Service. *The Opossum,* U.S.F.W.S. Leaflet No. 359, March, 1955.

Volk, Joseph J. *"Isospora boughtoni N. sp.* from the American Opossum, *Didelphis virginiana,"* *Journal of Parasitology,* Vol. 24, No. 6, December, 1938.

Walker, Ernest P.; *et al. Mammals of the World,* Johns Hopkins Press, Baltimore, 1964.

Wheeler, Robert J. "Food Habits of the Opossum in Sumter County, Alabama," unpublished master's thesis, Alabama Polytechnic Institute, 1939.

Wiedorn, William S. "A New Experimental Animal for Psychiatric Research, the Opossum, (D.V.)," *Science,* Vol. 119, p. 360, March, 1954.

Wiseman, George L., and George O. Hendrickson. "Notes on the Life History and Ecology of the Opossum in Southeast Iowa," *Journal of Mammalogy,* Vol. 31, No. 3, August, 1950.

Yeager, Lee E. "Winter Daytime Dens of the Opossum," *Journal of Mammalogy,* Vol. 17, No. 4, November, 1936.

Index

abundance, 107
adaptability, 54–56
aerial spraying, 106, 115
Arizona, 59, 105
Athens, Ga., 106
Australia, 29, 30, 55

Bailey, Vernon, 27
Baja California, 59
behavior, 79–90
birds, as food, 67, 100
birth, 44–46
bobcat, 91
bones, epipubic, 29
brain size, 27
breeding season, 43, 44
broken bones, 106
Brownington, Mo., 104, 113
Buel, Edward, 108

California, 59
Canada, 30, 31
carbon dioxide, 49
Carmen Possum, 124
carnivores, 65
carrion, 70
Celebes, 29
Central America, 30
Cherokee Indians, 108
chicken, as food, 66, 91, 113
chiggers, 105
chromosomes, 42
cold, effects of, 93, 94, 96, 97
Columbus, 13
Cook, Captain James, 30
corn, as food, 70
cottontail rabbit, as food, 70, 99

coyotes, 60, 91, 130
curiosity, 72
cuscus, 30
Cy Littlebee's Guide to Cooking Fish and Game, 121

Davis, Chester, 132
dens, 61, 101–104
Densmore, Frances, 109
dental formula, 64
description, 17 f.
development, 51–53
Didelphidae, 30
dieldrin, 106, 130
diet, 65–70, 98–101
dingos, 29
dog, as predator, 90, 106
Doutt, J. Kenneth, 57
duckbill (platypus), 29

ears, 93, 94
Eden, Richard, 112
eggs, 41, 42
epiglottis, 49
epipubic bones, 29
estrus, 43, 44
eyes, 27

farm ponds, 59
feet, 74
Fitch, Henry L., 88, 89
fleas, 106
Florida, 93
flukes, 106
foxes, 60, 91
fruit, as food, 68
fur, 18, 114–120

Georgia, 106, 123
Georgia Game and Fish magazine, 123
geotropism, negative, 46
Gessner, Konrad, 13
gestation, 43
glans, 40
gliding possum, 29
great gray kangaroo, 29
grooming, 76, 77

habitat, 33, 34
Harriot, Thomas, 113
Hartman, Carl G., 14, 19, 43, 45, 128
hearing, 27, 77
Heinze, Mrs. A. A., 122
Hennepin, Father, 113
Hesselschwert, R. E., 61
hibernation, 96
Higginsville, Mo., 121
Hock, Raymond, 105
home range, 38
homoiotherm, 48
Hopewell culture, 108
horned owl, 60, 91
hunting, 119–121
hunting dogs, 120–121

Illinois, 58, 61, 98, 100, 104, 106, 130
Imperial, Mo., 122
Indiana, 58, 113, 116
Indians, 108
insecticides, 106
insects, as food, 66–70
intelligence, 27, 28
Iowa, 58
Isospora, 106

Jefferson City, Mo., 70, 108

Kansas, 58, 88, 91, 98, 105
Klimstra, W. D., 98
koalas, 29, 55

La Salle, Rene Robert Cavelier,
    Sieur de, 113

Lawson, John, 107
Lay, Daniel W., 60
learning ability, 78, 79
Le Page du Pratz, Antoine, 107
Lesser Antilles, 3
Lincecum, G., 20, 61
Linné, Carl von, 15
litter: number of, 51
    size, 43
Llewellyn, L. M., 66, 67
longevity, 105

mammae, 29, 47, 48
mammals, 28
man, as predator, 91
marsupials, 28
Martyr, Peter, 13
Maryland, 66, 67
mating, 39
Mexico, 58, 108
Michel, Dr. Middleton, 44
Michigan, 58, 65, 72
Middle Mississippian culture, 108
Mississippi, 102
Missouri, 40, 43, 51, 58, 61, 68, 70, 76,
    104, 113, 116, 121, 122
Missouri Department of Conservation,
    121
mites, 106
Moluccas, 29

Nagel, W. O., 121
name, 13, 15, 16, 113
nematodes, 106
nests, 33
Newnan, Ga., 123
New York, 58
New Zealand, 24
North America, 29, 30

odor, 76, 77
Ohio, 58
Oklahoma, 58, 106
Ontario, 93
opossum:
    abundance, 107

opossum—*cont.*
adaptability, 54–56
behavior, 79–90
birth, 44–46
brain size, 27
breeding season, 43, 44
chromosomes, 42
curiosity, 72
dens, 61, 101–104
dental formula, 64
description, 17 f.
development, 51–53
diet, 65–70, 98–101
ears, 93, 94
eggs, 41, 42
eyes, 27
feet, 74
fur, 18, 114–120
gestation, 43
glans, 40
grooming, 76, 77
habitat, 33, 34
hearing, 27, 77
home range, 38
intelligence, 27, 28
learning ability, 78, 79
litter, number of, 51
litter size, 43
longevity, 105
mating, 39
name, 13, 15, 16, 113
nests, 33
odor, 76, 77
oestrus, 43, 44
parasites, 105, 106
penis, 39
as pets, 126
placenta, 43
"playing possum," 84–90
pouch, 17, 53
range, as species, 30, 56–64, 130
sex ratio, 104, 105
size, 17
smell, sense of, 27, 76
sociability, 38
swimming, 56, 57, 58

opossum—*cont.*
tail, 18–24, 93, 94
teats, 29, 47, 48
teeth, 64, 65
teeth, development of, 48
"thumb," 74
tracks, 74
vagina, 39
vibrissae (whiskers), 52
vision, 27
voice, 25, 52
wandering, 60–62
weight, 19
Oregon, 59

Paragonimus westermani, 106
parasites, 105, 106
penis, 39
Pennsylvania, 58
persimmon, as food, 70, 72
pets, 126
phalangers, 30
Philbert, 23
Pinzon, Vincente Yanez, 13
placenta, 43
placental mammals, 29
platypus, 29
"playing possum," 84–90
possum, 30
pouch, 17, 53
predators, 60, 90, 106
Pugh, Art, 121

raccoon, 27
range, as species, 30, 56–62, 64, 130
recipes, 121–122
Reelfoot Lake, Tenn., 106
reflex actions, 46
reptiles, as food, 68, 69
Reynolds, Harold C., 43, 45, 51, 57–59, 61, 62, 68, 69
ring-tailed opossums, 30
roundworms, 106

St. Joseph County, Ind., 113
Sandidge, Lewis L., 88, 89, 91

San Francisco, 59
scaly-tailed possum, 30
Schwartz, Charles W. and Elizabeth R.,
    59, 65
Science, 84
Seminole Indians, 109, 111
Seton, Ernest Thompson, 27, 58, 90
sex ratio, 104, 105
Sheldon, Ill., 106
size, 17
smell, sense of, 27, 76
Smith, Captain John, 13, 112
Smith, Luther, 20
snow, effects of, 93
sociability, 38
South America, 29, 30, 77
Spain, 13
spiny anteater, 29
Spirocerca longispiculata, 106
Stieglitz, Walter O., 98
swimming, 56–58

tail, 18–24, 93, 94
tapeworms, 106
teats, 29, 47, 48
teeth, 64, 65
teeth, development of, 48
Tennessee, 106
territory, 35, 38
Texas, 58

Thomas Arthur, 113
"thumb," 74
ticks, 105
Townsend, Dr. Charles H., 128
tracks, 74
trapping, 106, 114–120
tree kangaroos, 29
tularemia, 105
typhus fever, 105

Uhler, F. M. 66, 67
U. S. Bureau of Sports Fisheries
    & Wildlife, 116, 118

vagina, 39
vibrissae (whiskers), 52
vision, 27
voice, 25, 52
Voss, Mrs. Lola, 104, 113, 132

wandering, 60, 61, 62
Washington, 59
weight, 19
whales, 28
Wheeler National Wildlife Refuge, 106
Wiedorn, William S., 84, 88, 89, 92
wolves, 60

Yucatán, 108